Simon Caley was born in 1⁹
to Calcutta in 1958, and in 1962 – probably as a result of
his parents having suffered enough – was sent away to
school in the UK.

He was educated, from the age of eight to seventeen, at
Hurstpierpoint College, Sussex, from where, after taking a
year off, he went to Guy's Hospital, London, to qualify as a
Dental Surgeon.

He worked on the Isle of Wight, both at his own practice
and as the visiting dentist for HMPs Parkhurst, Albany and
Camphill before recently moving to Wales to pursue his real
love (no, not sheep) – writing: and the character of William
was born.

SIMON CALEY

WILLIAM'S WAY

Matador
9 De Montfort Mews
Leicester LE1 7FW, UK
Tel: (+44) 116 255 9311 / 9312
Email: books@troubador.co.uk
Web: www.troubador.co.uk/matador

This is a work of fiction. Characters, companies and locations are either the product of the
author's imagination or, in the case of locations, if real, used fictitiously without any
intent to describe their actual environment.

ISBN 978-1848761-414

A Cataloguing-in-Publication (CIP) catalogue record for this book
is available from the British Library.

Illustrations by Daniel Jeffery

Typeset in 11pt Book Antiqua by Troubador Publishing Ltd, Leicester, UK
Printed in the UK by TJ International, Padstow, Cornwall

Matador is an imprint of Troubador Publishing Ltd

Dedicated to
Maxine, Ashley and Georgia.

My thanks to Ute Methner and Bill Coleman for their help with some of the finer details – as well as for not pushing me off the top of Aiguille du Tour when they had the chance.

Illustrations by
Daniel Jeffery
www.djillustrator.com

WILLIAM'S WAY

The Beginning.

I am, as many who know me will readily attest, a simple sort of fellow: someone who would like his tombstone to read 'Here lies William; pleasant enough, he negotiated Life without bothering too many people'. A minimal social footprint, so to speak.

I will admit, however, to having one or two traits that some might misconstrue as bloody-mindedness; but I prefer to think of them as 'Heart of Oak' material: a 'Body of England breathing English air' and so forth. Anyway, there I was, trundling along, well on course to achieving my desired obituary when ... To paraphrase a line from the work of a certain Dylan Thomas, perhaps I had better 'begin at the beginning'.

Although, now I come to think about it, it does seem rather difficult to know where to start a tale which tells of a passage in one's life that has, almost certainly, had a profound effect on the way one thinks about a great many things.

Then, apart from where to begin, there is also the question of when. Should I have started yesterday? Perhaps I should begin tomorrow. Both of those options are perfectly acceptable, and had I started yesterday I should, almost certainly, be further along than I am today. But had tomorrow been my favoured option, then I, almost equally certainly, wouldn't be anywhere near my laptop. No, I should, more than likely, be pottering about in my garden; or sitting, with a cup of tea, watching the test match between England and India. Not at the ground, you understand, but whilst enjoying the comfort provided by the armchair in front of my television.

Now, before you make some fatuous remark about 'armchair' sportsmen, I should add that I have occasionally

1

partaken in the game that is also known as the 'Metaphor for Life', and that I often went to various grounds to watch a cricket match. But I, like many others I am sure, have unwittingly become addicted to the scourge of many umpires: I refer, of course, to the action replay.

Sport, and life in general, seemed so simple before the arrival of television analysis: certainly in the game of cricket. After all, there was a time when a batsman never showed dissent. Oh no. He simply accepted the umpire's decision with cordial equanimity, slipped the length of willow under his arm and made a dignified exit from the field of play. Similarly, the same fellow would also 'walk' if he felt that the opposition had made a good catch - despite it having slipped the umpire's eye. Even fielders could be relied upon to tell the truth if they felt that the leather had made contact with the green stuff before taking up residence within the confines of their fingers.

But these days? Goodness! Hardly a match goes by without some form of discord being displayed. Even downright cheating has been known to occur. Is money behind it all? Probably. I don't even want to start on my thoughts (and may I say that they are plentiful) about the effects that Messrs Packer and Murdoch might well have contributed to the overall character of the game. The moral must surely be that one should hand out knighthoods to antipodeans before they cause too much damage.

Anyway, I must confess to a predilection for listening to TMS – 'Test Match Special' for the uninitiated. I must also confess to extreme annoyance at the way that certain individuals (who obviously thought they knew best) kept switching around its location on the radio dial. What, I ask, was wrong with where it was when it occupied the Radio 3 medium-wave berth? Nearly all of the personal radios had medium-wave, and thus allowed many a chap to listen to the test match commentary whilst working in his shed, driving in his car, or – with judicious handling and a covert earphone in place – whilst accompanying his better half on a shopping excursion.

Next, I seem to recall, there was a brief dalliance with a couple of other slots on the Medium Wave before they went and hid TMS somewhere within the morass that is Long Wave. Why? There must have been countless thousands of unfortunates who did not possess a small radio that contained a Long Wave receiving facility. I often wondered if the people responsible for the move had shares in a firm that made radios that could receive Long Wave: or am I merely venting the Phalarope streak of cynicism? As for my reaction to matters concerning 'Five Live' ... Well, once again, least said soonest mended.

However, my preferred modus operandi - along with, I am sure, many others of a similar inclination – was watching a game on the television whilst enjoying the radio commentary employing the dulcet tones of Johnson, Blofeld, Arlot and Bailey: and therein lies the cause of my problem. I, as I mentioned earlier, had become used to the action replay. I wanted to know by exactly how many thousandths of an inch the ball had missed the stumps: I wanted to know by how many thousandths of a second the batsman had mistimed his stroke: I wanted to know details about matters that I previously never knew could be timed; nor, for that matter, actually existed.

This state of affairs, so I believe, is very much symptomatic of our society these days. Exempli Gratia - in the 1950s, one would have to wind up one's watch (or mantle clock) and speak proudly of the way that it only lost (or gained) no more than a minute a day. These days, with all the quartz contributions, one is aggrieved if one's timepiece mislays so much as half a second a year: and then – with the intervention of one of that type who, when I consider the contributions that certain organisms make to the overall pleasantness of Life, occupies the shelf immediately below the wasp and is known as the compensation lawyer – one is tempted to sue for whatever one can argue.

I do hope that I am not the only person who feels that such pimples should be squeezed at the earliest opportunity. So your son walked into a swing at the playground and you want to sue somebody: so why don't you go and get his eyes tested? Or, better still, embrace your parental responsibility a little more firmly and teach him how to safely use the facilities that have been provided.

Maybe Frederick W. Pomeroy should have sculpted 'Justice' in the act of chasing an ambulance.

Perhaps I shall live to see the day when children can sue their parents for handing out genes that in any way run the risk of causing their new owner to behave in the same crass manner as that which their immediate forebears displayed.

However, to return to my initial thread, I decided to start my written record today: and so here I am, in front of my laptop, fingers flexed and ready to go. I say 'fingers', but I really only mean two of them; and, occasionally, a thumb. Not for me the dextrous flair of a seasoned touch-typist: no, rather more the maladroit manoeuvrings of someone more used to having a 14lb sledge-hammer in his hands. Still.

I also have, within easy reach, a cup of tea: although, strictly speaking, it is a mug of tea. I have always found that cups require saucers, and a jolly sight more refills than mugs: and that means more movement: and more washing up. All of which, for someone cursed since birth with a desire to expend as little energy as possible, can be most unsettling.

I am not, by nature, a lazy person - although I fear a lot of those who know me may testify otherwise – it is just that I regard my reserves of energy as being rather valuable, and something to conserve wisely. One never knows when they might be called upon.

Anyway, here I am, so occupied because of an incident that occurred a couple of months ago. Not an incident with which I was connected in the actual happening of same, but one in which I subsequently became involved. I ... That doesn't sound all that clear, does it? Let me try and elucidate.

I possess a sister - although, upon reflection, I don't suppose that I actually 'possess' her. Perhaps I 'have' a sister would be more accurate. Yes; I think 'have' is a better description: I have a sister. Her name is Lynne, and she used to be about three years older than me.

Now I expect you are wondering what it is I mean when I say 'used to be'. I have always been under the impression that she is older than me – by about three years: or at least she was when I was in my teens - and, perhaps rather foolishly, I had assumed that she would remain three years older than me for as long as we both continued to walk the ever-steepening road that Life always seems anxious we follow.

I can remember being harangued by expressions such as "No you can't come and play with me and my friends. You're only thirteen, and I'm sixteen, for goodness sake," and "You're just a spotty oik – a kid who knows nothing of where people my age are at," and "Call me when you're grown-up."

At the time, I seem to recall my sister's calculation to have been accurate. I was thirteen years old and she, as she stressed upon my youthful cognitive powers, was sixteen. So, unless my prep school years under the tutelage of certain mathematics teacher by the name of Mr Hill were a complete waste of time, I would have estimated that I was, indeed, three years younger than my sibling: and, I had presumed, would always remain thus.

However, of late, it seems that dear Lynne has taken to ageing in a most peculiar fashion. Id est – she has either been ignoring tempus as it fugits, or subtracting instead of adding the passing years onto those she has already endured. I am absolutely certain, when last I last heard her discussing the matter, that she said she was forty-four.

Now that, I hasten to stress, in itself is no crime: a tad confusing, perhaps, as I was fairly sure that I had recently celebrated my forty-ninth birthday. Inevitably I did spend some time wondering what might have occurred. Perhaps she had discovered some magic elixir that has allowed her to do what she pleases with the passage of time.

Perhaps Thomas Campbell was wrong when he wrote ...

> Heaven gives our years of fading strength
> Indemnifying fleetness;
> And those of youth, a seeming length,
> Proportioned to their sweetness.

Perhaps he meant to write ...

> Heaven gives us urge whilst on this Earth,
> To stand in centre stage;
> Then men oft lie about their girth,
> And women 'bout their age.

Anyway, possible timekeeping deceptions aside, Lynne has two progeny – a boy and a girl – who are, without doubt, the best walking advertisements for contraception upon which it has ever been my misfortune to stumble. Ghastly would be too kind a word to describe them. Abhorrent and repulsive are getting closer. Twins, aged twelve years apiece, named Tarquin and Mirabella.

I can distinctly recall - at their christening – asking the person standing next to me if I had heard correctly, and wondering if the acoustics within the confines of the chapel were, perhaps, a little below par. Tarquin and Mirabella! I ask you. Small wonder that they have developed into the twin forces of evil they are today.

Perhaps it might have been more convenient had their mother belonged to the Yoruba tribe of Nigeria where, so I understand, they have a tendency to destroy twins at birth: and sometimes the mother as well.

Lynne's two heirs seldom seem able to negotiate a day without picking on some poor individual or other, and making

6

them fall prey to one of their less-than-whimsical pranks. It is, obviously, more acceptable if the focus of their jocularity is a complete stranger – only in so much as the butt of their mirth is therefore not yours truly, or anyone who may know that the three of us are in any way related – but still one cannot help feeling a degree of compassion for the person concerned.

Personally, I find that jokes tend to wear a bit thin after one has heard – or seen, or even experienced – them several times. For some jokes, I might add, fewer times are required than for others. However, I have to admit to being mildly amused when the twins put some Liver Salts (belonging to a fellow called Andrew) into a sugar bowl that was then passed to an unsuspecting relative by the name of Aunt Laura.

Although Aunt Laura was known as 'Aunt', I do not believe that there was any genetic link to the Phalarope clan – apart from those that separate Homo Sapiens from the rest of the animated world. Mind you, there would have been no cause for embarrassment had there been. Laura was a dear old soul, who was always pleased to see you, and who always had time for a friendly word and a cup of tea. She was also the type of person who was constantly bemoaning her lot … and her back, hip, sciatica, arthritis, and some other conditions that I was quite sure were only to be found in ovine circles. And yet, when she had a gin and tonic in one hand and a Player's Capstan in the other, she would be able to spring from her chair and leap around the room, spraying everyone with saliva, as she recounted her halcyon days. Great value for money, I have to say - as long as you had time to dry out before your next appointment.

Anyhow, if you'll pardon the pun, back to the issue in hand – the twin tormentors, the bowl of sugar, and Andrew's Liver Salts. Aunt Laura had no sooner dropped a couple of heaped teaspoons of the white granules into her beverage when the cup of tea that she was stirring began to bubble and froth in a manner that was more akin to an over-soaped washing machine; with the unexpected (to me at any rate) addition that the froth then

7

set hard, practically wresting the teaspoon from Aunt Laura's grasp.

Had one's list of working expletives been less than comprehensive, Aunt Laura burst forth with a selection that would have adequately filled a lot of the empty spaces. Then, when she had fathomed the agents of her discomposure, she displayed a turn of speed that was only marginally outmatched by that shown by the twins.

I think I can feel a question about to emerge from the readers, à propos the issue in question. Is it not, I sense you formulating, a wee bit unusual that Lynne – who is almost certainly comfortably into her fifties – has children who are only twelve years old? Has she been the unwitting subject of some IVF experiment that went awry? I don't think so. Was the conception immaculate? I rather doubt it. I think the only type of ghost (holy or otherwise) likely to stray anywhere near her nether regions would be a poltergeist that had been mingling with the wrong kind of spirits – those of 40% in nature, to be exact - for most of the evening.

No, I fear that the cause of her parenthood at such a comparatively late stage in life was due to her having indulged in some conjugal unpleasantness with a rather disagreeable smell that occasionally manifests itself as her husband. A fellow by the name of Geremy: yes, with a 'G'. Geremy. I ask you!

Perhaps if I took the time to closely study the writings of a certain Gregor Johann Mendel, I might be better able to explain the source of the genetic aberration that resulted in their joint progeny. I am fairly sure that the DNA chiefly responsible for such a pair of anarchic anthropoids did not come from my side of the family, and so I cannot be expected to hold up my hand to claim culpability on that score.

"But hang on a second: isn't your sister from your side of the family? Don't you share a common source?" I hear you ask.

"Ostensibly," I would reply; but my repudiation offers the possibility that perhaps the code skips several generations, and is only carried by an unsuspecting female member of the family.

And, further surmising would suggest, the gene responsible would have to be of the recessive variety – the second helping having been donated by the merdivorous Geremy - as had it been of a dominant character, those unfortunately burdened with the affliction would have been ostracised from society before their tenth birthday and would, therefore, have been denied the opportunity to pass on the offending trait.

Upon a further reflection, I can recall my mother speaking of a distant cousin of hers – Ebbsworth - who spent a great deal of his time balancing on a unicycle, clutching a large tumbler of twelve year-old malt, whilst reciting Thomas Gray's 'Ode on the death of a favourite cat, drowned in a tub of goldfishes'. Now, don't get me wrong, I find lines such as ...

'Eight times emerging from the flood
   She mew'd to ev'ry watry God,
     Some speedy aid to send'.

... more than stirring a'plenty. Furthermore, I agree with the notion about all that glisters not being gold, and I am always happy to endorse the benefits of having a hobby: but I feel that poetry is best enjoyed from a reclining position. I do, however, completely endorse the large tumbler of a twelve year-old malt.

But, to return to the subject of rogue chromosomes, my mother did add that poor Ebbsworth had once been dropped on his head whilst a baby. Perhaps that might account for the anomaly on our side of the family. I wonder if Darwin had ever considered such possibilities when composing his theory of evolution. Perhaps Empedocles (circa 450BC) gave it mention in one of his treatises on the subject of the way living things alter with time: and those, by the way, apart from being penned more than two millennia before Darwin, were always written in verse. Clever chap, eh?

Goodness, I appear to have digressed even further than my previous excursion: so, I had better return to the reason for my current status.

It seems that my niece and nephew decided, for some reason best known to them, to enter my name into a competition that appeared in some weekly magazine. Or was it a monthly publication? I can't remember, but no matter as I don't think it really makes a great deal of difference.

The competition, so I was to discover, was for people to nominate someone – preferably a family member – who was in need of ... I think the term used was 'a makeover'. But not merely in the sartorial department: oh no: it transpired that the organisers wanted to indulge in something of a philosophical nature as well. In other words, they intended to take the recipient of the first prize and alter him, or her, in whatever ways the editorial staff of the periodical felt would best increase its circulation.

"Fair enough," one might say, especially given the economic vicissitudes that are currently swirling around us. "Whatever is needed to keep people in gainful employment, and off the streets: and a very loud 'Hurrah' to that."

Hurrah indeed: unless it is your good self that is the focus of such munificence: or, as it transpired in this particular case, me.

Now don't get me wrong. I am sure there are plenty of people who think I might benefit from some well-intentioned guidance in the clothes, hair and personality departments: and, almost certainly, in several other departments as well. But, I, however, am not in agreement: neither total nor partial.

You see, I have managed, for the majority of the last forty-nine years – certainly the last thirty of them - to ensure that I do not upset, alarm, or otherwise inconvenience those whose paths happen to cross with mine. I will hold up my hand and admit that I am not always the first choice of person to occupy the seat next to you on a journey of longer than fifteen minutes (sometimes that allowance may not even exceed five minutes), but I feel that I can confidently put that down to a deficiency in the intellectual capacity of my fellow traveller rather than to any shortcomings of my own.

So why a perfect stranger should feel – as the result of a nomination by two children who would have made Genghis Khan wish that he had heeded his physician's advice to have a vasectomy – that I might welcome an opportunity to alter a situation that has been perfectly acceptable to me for many years is utterly beyond my ken. But do so they did.

The telephone in my home rang at ten-thirty in the morning on the day – a Tuesday, as it so happens - in question. I know that for a fact as I was there when it rang.

"What were you doing at home at ten-thirty on a Tuesday morning?" I hear you ask; rapidly followed by "Shouldn't you have been partaking of some financially remunerative activity?"

In the normal course of events I suppose that I should have. However, having been lumbered with a congenital form of dilatoriness, and having fortuitously made some judicious investments with a bequeathed largesse several years ago, I have been able, thus far, to negotiate most of my adult life without recourse to perspiring at another man's behest.

Now, before you all raise a hand to ask for advice regarding investing, I should add that my choice of speculation was largely down to luck and an ability to completely misread a certain paragraph in the Financial Times. It might also be germane at this point to add that I do not generate a great deal of revenue by these means. If I were to indulge myself in a trope concerning peregrination, I would say that I do not possess sufficient funds to allow me to travel *how* I like – merely enough to permit me to travel *when* I like. A subtle, but nevertheless salient, distinction.

Back to the ringing phone. I do so dislike the sound of a ringing phone: whether they warble, blurp, or sound like an ambulance rushing through your living-room. Why can't the manufacturers of said means of verbal communication construct a telephone that politely coughs to attract your attention? If, after several attempts, no perceivable contact has been made with the object of the telephone's endeavours then, by all means, embark upon a more boisterous agency. Perhaps a sonorous 'Yoo-hoo' would be apt.

While I'm on the subject of telephones, I should like to mention my antipathy towards the use of mobile telephones in certain environs. Any use of these appliances in public places that are enhanced (or actually designed to be enjoyed) by moments of tranquillity, should be severely punished. Furthermore, if the words "I'm on the train/bus/tube" are spoken on any of the aforementioned, then the telephone should be programmed to melt against the user's ear, and remain there for several weeks so that others may point and pour scorn upon him or her.

As I'm hovering near the subject of ambulances ... why, oh why, did the powers that be do away with the bells on ambulances, and replace them with the ghastly American-style 'whoo-whoo' that they currently employ?

In the good old days of Emergency Ward Ten and Dixon of Dock Green, everybody knew and could easily differentiate the sounds emitted by ambulances, fire engines and police cars. Wonderfully clear, ringing tones that let one know what was approaching: and how heartening it was to see the other road-users pull out of the way. No confusion between an emergency and an errant car alarm back then: and no chance of being caught on CCTV and then issued with a fine for edging one's car a few feet through a red traffic light so as to allow the Emergency Service's vehicle to get past.

Anyway, the telephone kept ringing, disturbing my reveries; so I eventually picked it up. I seem to recall the conversation going thus ...

"Hello." (That was me.)

"Is that Mr William Phalarope?" (That was the person speaking to me.)

"Yes."

"Mr Phalarope of Dilettante Cottage, Upper Lea?"

"Yes," I said. "I am he."

"Oh ... right. You were entered in a competition that 'Your Life' was running."

"I was?"

"Yes, and, I'm delighted to tell you that you have won."

There followed a silence.

"Mr Phalarope ... are you still there?"

"Yes."

"Did you hear what I just said?"

"I believe so."

"Oh ... good. Right. Um ... do you have any comment?"

"Other than I have no idea what it is about which you are speaking?"

"Other than ... about ... Oh. Um. No idea?"

"None whatsoever, I'm afraid."

"Er ... Do you know a Tarquin and Mirabella Thickett?"

"How old are they?"

"How old ...? Let me see ..." I could hear some paper being rustled. "Twelve years old."

"Oh ... them. Unfortunately, yes, I believe I do. Why?"

"Because they are the ones who entered you in the competition."

"Really." Oh joy. Yet another justification for removing those two guttersnipes from my Christmas card list: and that brought the list of reasons to one hundred and twenty-seven.

Anyway, to sidestep a rather long, and rather uninteresting exchange of words, the caller went on to inform me

13

that – in two weeks' time - someone from their magazine would be calling round to my cottage in order to discuss what they had in mind for me. Delighted and over-flowing with excitement would not have been an accurate description of my emotional state at the time; but, as I had very little pencilled in my social diary for the dates in question, I agreed to go along with the schedule.

Meeting Jocelyn

The twice-repeated opening two notes of the Cuckoo Waltz informed me that someone had pressed my front-door bell. Not exactly an over-imaginative choice of refrain I have to admit, but non-inflammatory nonetheless. I had thought about getting a doorbell that played the Westminster chimes, Greensleeves, or even, possibly, the Marseillaise; but having an IQ in excess of my age and a desire not to be mocked by visitors prevented me from making that mistake.

Ah, the Marseillaise. When I was at my prep school – an institution, by the way, whose aims loitered somewhere amongst wanting to prepare boys as young as eight for a range of skills that included gaining accreditation in society, dedicating oneself to finding a cure for every conceivable malaise that existed on this wonderful planet of ours, being able to laugh about apple-pie beds (usually one's own), and spending a wet Friday afternoon outside the chapel beating a rug with a hockey stick until every atom of dust had been dispersed to the atmosphere – there existed a French teacher: who, by the way, also taught geography and English.

And, I have to say, no ordinary French teacher was he: not by a long chalk. I have memories of being made – as a complete class, and not as a result of having been singled out – to stand on

14

our chairs and sing, with as much gusto as a room full of nine year-old boys could manage without causing permanent damage to their developing viscera, the first verse of the Marseillaise. I think he (our teacher – a Mr Maxwell as I recall, who wasn't actually French, you understand, just taught it as a subject) would have liked us to complete all seven verses, but by the time we had sung about slitting the throats of various people's sons, there was usually quite a crowd of other pupils, and teachers, standing outside the windows of our class-room.

Now whether it was the natural modesty of my fellow classmates or a desire not to be ribbed mercilessly during the lunch-break I shall never know, but the subsequent verses were never reached. I can remember hoping that Claude-Joseph Rouget de Lisle understood, and forgave, our reluctance: which, I might add, I rather think he would have. A bit of an enigma, was Msr Rouget de Lisle. It seems that he was quite a staunch royalist! He refused to take the oath of allegiance to the new constitution, was imprisoned, and only narrowly escaped the guillotine!

But regardless of history, and despite all that eccentricity, Mr Maxwell was a superb French teacher. And chapeaux off to him, say I.

I seem to have strayed once again. Now where was I? Oh yes, my doorbell and the Cuckoo Waltz.

The person I found standing on my doorstep was an individual around twenty-five years old, of a female persuasion, and wearing what I can only describe as attire more commonly found on a garage mechanic. She had very short hair, an unflattering pair of spectacles, and what appeared to be the sort of

15

footwear normally worn by commandos when they embark upon some dangerous night-time operation. The resultant combination gave her the bearing of a lady unlikely to be found asking questions at the make-up counter of any high street shops.

I fear that my sense of shock must have somehow got involved in the control of my physical movements, for I suddenly took several steps in a backward direction. On top of which, I think my jaw may have dropped open; thus adding to the unmistakeable appearance of alarm on my part.

The young lady then took a couple of backward steps as well, which induced me to move further away: and then she felt compelled to increase the distance between us even more. I think it was just as well I chose that moment to trip over the umbrella that I had left leaning against the wall - and standing in a pint mug in order to catch the drips as it dried out after having used it to go and feed my fish during the shower of rain that had visited earlier that morning – or else we may never have caught sight of each other again.

Did I mention that I have a fishpond in my garden? No? Well I have. It's not a big one – the pond, rather than the garden – and measures about ten feet by five. I'm not sure a garden that measured ten feet by five would ever be described as big. Unless you lived in a flat, and then, I should imagine, any sized garden would be regarded as big: especially if you had plonked it in the middle of your lounge.

Anyway, my fishpond. There are twelve fishes present, but I am unable to tell you exactly what sorts they are; other than one is black (with a mouth rather like a letter-box), five are a gold colour, two are red with black spots, three a pale pink, and the last one is grey and rather fat. I take it upon myself to feed said fishes at least once a day (I chuck a few of those dreadful-smelling pea-sized brown pellet things into the pond) – except between November and March when I conduct the procedure on a weekly basis as they never seem to eat much during that time.

My postman once said to me "That's because they hibernate during the winter months."

"Do they?" I replied, unsure if he was being serious. I had a close look at his trouser legs to see if they displayed any tell-tale signs of having been attacked by a bull mastiff earlier that morning: just in case, you understand, he had decided to vent his spleen by having a joke at my expense. His trousers were still intact. "Oh, I never knew that."

"Yes. Unless they are warm-water fish. And then they eat all year round."

"Oh."

"Yes."

Well, as they say, you learn something new every day. Or do they say that you are *supposed* to learn something new every day? I can't remember. And I don't recall if they ever mentioned *how* one is supposed to learn something new every day. Or what one has to do if, for example, one spent the entire day asleep. Do you have to learn two things the following day? Or what if finding out that you don't really mind missing a day's intake counts as learning something? And what if ... Oh dear, this circular thinking has made me feel quite faint.

Anyway, I know one or two coves who would quite gladly spend twenty-four hours staring at the inside of their eyelids, and not give a jot of care about missing the chance of adding to their somewhat inconsiderable mental data-bases.

Doorbell ... female personage ... tripping over umbrella. Yes, and just as well I did; else I fear that said female and I might well have had to conduct our conversation by shouting at each other through cupped hands or rolled-up newspapers, such was our apparent desire to continue jumping backwards away from each other.

A truce was tacitly arranged; and I carefully approached my visitor, who turned out to be a representative of the publication in whose competition I had unwittingly triumphed. Then, after having manoeuvred our way through the necessary

17

introductions and apologies (for my overly-vigorous recoiling), I invited the young lady – who answered to the name of Ms Jocelyn Forsopition ... or Josh (as Jocelyn, as I was later informed, apparently liked to be called – unless she was speaking with, or writing to, a complete stranger, in which case she preferred to be called Ms Forsopition) - into my humble abode.

Do you ever meet people whose names would make everybody smile if just a couple of letters was swapped around? I was going to point this out to Ms Forsopition but decided against doing so: and just as well I didn't, as I soon came to realise that Ms Forsopition was not the kind of person who would have fully appreciated the fact.

Now call me 'old-fashioned' by all means, but I have never quite understood the forcefulness with which some women insist on the 'Ms' prefix – usually, I have noticed, pronounced Mzzz. Do they imagine it lends them gravitas? Do they suppose that having others know their marital, or otherwise, status is going to belittle them in any way? There was I thinking that a ring on the third finger of the left hand was designed for that purpose. Not the belittling, you understand, just the state of any union. Anyway, I have always felt that 'Miss' is a rather handy title because it would inform any potential suitors as to the lady's singularity: and 'Mrs' is equally useful, as it would apprise potential suitors that the lady was already spoken for and would greatly appreciate not being pestered.

In retrospect, however, perhaps the dungarees and short hair ought to have given me a sharp poke in the ribs. But regardless of her inclinations, Ms Forsopition then nattered on, at length I might add, about what winning the competition was going to entail, and she described the most alarming array of clauses and sub-clauses to which I had to adhere, or at the very least acknowledge, otherwise the deal was off.

It was about this time that I became aware of something about Ms Forsopition that had, hitherto, escaped my normally observant nature – videlicet her rather tinny (and some might

18

have added whiney) American accent. I would not describe myself as being an expert on variations in enunciation - especially those brought about by the geographical locations in which one underwent most of one's elocution training - but I do pride myself on being able to spot vocal tones (by tones I mean pronunciation, rather than any arrogant inflection used to deliver the words) that hail from the far side of the Atlantic Ocean. Not from which part of the North American continent – except, possibly, a Texan 'drawl' (or is that called a 'twang'?)– or whether the accent happens to be American or Canadian, I have to say; but I can certainly tell the continent.

I am also rather good at spotting accents from the Indian subcontinent; only I'm never sure whether the skin colour or the detected brogue of the orator is what leads me to reach my deduction. Perhaps a small clue might be obtained from the fact that I have been known, when in subdued lighting, to speak with the owner of such an accent about the shame regarding the closure of so many mines in the Rhondda.

Similarly, I once spent several minutes in a hostelry talking about my childhood in Calcutta to a gentleman that I had understood to be from Bengal - only to find that his name was Rhoddri Evans and that he was on his way home from a shift in Penrhiwceiber. Apparently the colliery showers had broken down that afternoon and, as he lived fairly close, he had decided to walk home to wash away the residue from his toils, and stopped off for a swift half on the way. In my defence, I would say that, for me, it was an easy mistake to make: and I feel sure that many others would also have done so with consummate ease.

Jocelyn. Oh yes, the contract. She produced several sheets of official-looking paper to which I was asked to add my moniker. I nearly called it my 'John Hancock' then.

"Your what?" I can hear people asking.

"My John Hancock. Just a small consequence from my coming experiences."

"Nope; no clearer, I'm afraid," they further say.

"It will be."

"You're barking, you know, and should not be allowed out unaccompanied."

"Have patience."

Anyway, the contract. I have to admit to being a bit of a nincompoop when it comes to reading contracts. It seems that whenever the typed word is smaller than (what I believe is commonly referred to as) font size 12, my cognitive processes seem to go haywire. I don't just mean slightly haywire: I mean that the letters appear to start sticking out their tongues whilst waggling their fingers in their ears, before they all merge into an amorphous mass that wriggles about like a plate piled high with wriggly things. Then, so I believe, as a finale, the letters join together and begin to make elaborate pictures. Some of them are quite impressive; both from an artistic point of view and the fact that there is no break in the line. I, however, have not been privileged to witness much of same as, by this stage, I am usually lying down somewhere requiring a moist cloth to be gently applied to my forehead.

But, with more than a dash of rashness, sign the aforementioned contract I did. I afforded myself some solace, however, in that should I subsequently be expected to partake of anything that went against my signally distinctive grain, I would cry "foul" on account of having signed the contract under duress.

I then decided, whilst both Ms Forsopition and I were smiling, to enquire if she would like a cup of tea. She said that she would be delighted, and would I make the slice of lemon a generous one.

Now call me a traditionalist, if you must, and stuck in the ways of the old world, but the thought of putting a slice of lemon - of whatever dimension - into a cup of tea had never occurred to me. I do not even care for the idea of adding sugar. I have always thought that the whole point of drinking tea was to enjoy the taste of the tea: not the taste of the sugar, or the lemon, or whatever else one is possessed to add. Milk, and milk alone. If you want a cup of hot lemon, then ask for one; that's what I say.

Before all you experts leap to your feet and shout – in, no doubt, very loud voices – that there are more than 3,000 varieties of tea ... I already know: and I also know a certain amount about certain tea-drinking customs that are performed in certain parts of the world. I, as it so happens, prefer the custom originated by the Duchess of Bedford (in about 1840 I believe) and, with the possible addition of a buttered scone or cream cake on the side, I like my tea with nothing more in it than a small serving of milk.

The milk, in my opinion, should always be cold, semi-skimmed, and put in the cup first. I do not, however, have any hard (or fast) rules about how long the boiling water and the tea-leaves should remain in contact with one another, or whether said contact should be referred to as 'effusing' or 'drawing'. Furthermore, I do not have any strict ideas on which blend of the Camellia Sinensis species is used; provided the tea doesn't taste flowery, or herby, or look as though it either has to be chewed or helped out of the cup.

However, as luck would have it, I didn't possess any lemon, because a good friend of mine – one Alun Haise (a local general practitioner) – had called round the previous evening to partake of some imbibing of a drink distilled from malted grain and flavoured with juniper berries that had been cautiously diluted with carbonated water containing quinine: and ice: and the erstwhile available lemon.

"Would milk do?" I enquired politely, as I didn't particularly want Ms Forsopition to adopt an aggressive nature.

"What kind?"

What kind of milk? Did she mean was it from a cow or from a goat? Perhaps, if a cow was her preferred donor, she would have liked 'gold top'. Although, on reflection, she didn't look old enough to remember 'gold top'. Gold top, you may or may not recall, was milk that still had all the cream in it; and it came – that is, it was delivered to your doorstep – in a bottle with

21

a gold top. Not a hugely imaginative name for a bottle with a gold top to it, but accurate enough to leave one in no doubt as to which bottle it was. The other choices were silver and red: or at least they were in my part of the world. I think, upon further reflection, that there may even have been one that was green. But what if she asked for Soya?

Further confused deliberations on my part were curtailed with the reply "Do you have sem-my skimmed?"

Why some people have to pronounce 'sem-me' as 'sem-my' I don't know. But, there again, she was American; so, I suppose, it was to be expected. Anyhow, as I just mentioned, that was the very same sort of milk that I prefer to use, and so 'sem-my' was what she got.

Tea was duly served, and Ms Forsopition then described what the prize entailed. I was to be taken to a men's outfitter — chosen by the publication - where I was to be 'outfitted' with various garments that would either prove appropriate or stand me in good stead whilst I spent time at the location that had also been chosen by the publication.

"How do you feel about going away for six weeks?" she asked me.

"I think that would rather depend on where I was going," I replied, having easy recall to what was actually a week - but seemed like six - spent on the Isle of Wight one very wet October a few years before. I would like to make it clear that I do not wish to demean in any way the island named Vectis by some rather enterprising Italians around 43AD. Nor do I wish to draw attention to the fact that the IOW was possibly the last part of Britain to be introduced to Christianity: and, probably, the last part of Britain to be introduced to a lot of other things as well. No, I just thought I would mention the fact that I had spent seven days of my life marooned on a piece of land situated offshore from Portsmouth and Southampton, and make the point that Elysium it was not.

Once again, don't get me wrong; the Isle of Wight is a very pleasant piece of land, and I have heard it described as a microcosm for the rest of the British Isles. I have also heard it described as a whole load of other things: and not all of them complimentary, by any means. Although I should point out that the comments that could be described as being of a derogatory nature were mainly from people waiting to get their car aboard one of the ferries that transports vehicles to and from the Island: or waiting to get a job of work done: or crawling along behind one of the 'signal-free' tractors that frequent most of the Island's narrow, pot-holed roads.

As I said, I do not wish to denigrate the Isle of Wight (original meaning of 'Wight' was – so I believe – to split or divide ... related to the way that the island divided the waters of Portsmouth and Southampton), and stress that it has been a few years since I was there; but in all my years of driving motor vehicles I have never encountered drivers with as unique an attitude to the use of the Queen's highways as those to be found thereabouts. It seemed to me that the majority of them could be equally divided into one of two camps.

The first holds with the notion that if you drive a particular stretch of road for more than one calendar year, then that stretch of road becomes your property, to do with (and on) as you please. You can opt for either side of the road upon which to drive, at a speed of your choosing, and you never have to use signals of any description - except of a disparaging quality. The reason for the lack of signals is, apparently, that as you use the road on a near-daily basis, the other road users should know what your next move is going to be. This theory occurred to me when I noticed that IOW drivers tended to look at other drivers, rather than other cars, so they, presumably, would always be able to give a wave of recognition when they passed.

The second camp has, apparently, spoken with God, who has told them that they will never be involved in a road-traffic accident. But if (God, obviously, not forbidding) they are, it will only be a very minor one that will not involve casualties of any description.

And, joy of joys, it seemed that members of both camps were prone to holding enormous, and seemingly spontaneous, rallies whenever I decided to take my automobile for a quick spin along some of the many narrow thoroughfares that the IOW has to offer.

I did once hear that Queen Victoria decided, after extensive consultation, that it might be a good idea to install a garrison on the IOW: ostensibly for the purpose of maintaining a vigilant show of strength that would dissuade any continentals from aspirations above their station. However, there circulated a rumour that mentioned the real purpose of the army personnel was to dilute a gene pool that had grown so condensed that one could practically walk across it. But far be it from me to cast, or even perpetuate, any aspersions. Absolutely not.

"San Francisco," came the totally unexpected reply.

At that point I started to choke on small piece of scone — laden, incidentally, with a liberal helping of butter and jam — that was in the process of passing over my epiglottis before descending the length of my oesophagus. This had the result of producing a fit of coughing: not the often heard 'ahem-hem' type, but one that was more along the lines of 'have-you-ever-seen-the-inside-of-my-lungs-before?' variety.

I rather think that Ms Forsopition had rapidly reached the conclusion that she might be going to have to present the prize to a cadaver. Whilst that in itself shouldn't have belittled the value of the prize in any way, I think she probably felt that it might have made any photographic recording of the presentation a little awkward: and my acceptance speech somewhat lacklustre.

Before I had time to comprehensively contemplate eternity in the hereafter, Ms Forsopition leaped to her feet and, with a rather alarming wail, proceeded to thump me between the shoulder blades with sufficient force to not merely dislodge the offending piece of scone (which, by then, I had almost got back

24

under control) but also to nearly displace several inter-vertebral discs at the same time: specifically, those in the thoracic region of my spinal column. Had I known in advance of that vigorous assault upon my person, I may well have pondered awhile on the relative merits of dying by asphyxiation and living with paraplegia.

But time was of the essence, and Ms Forsopition was a woman (I don't think she would mind if I called her thus) of action; and I shall for ever be grateful for her quickness of thought: and the fact that she used the heel of her hand and not the shin-length, reinforced boots that she was sporting at the time.

"San Francisco?" I finally managed, when the normal passage of air to my alveoli had been restored.

"Yes. San Francisco."

"For six weeks?"

"Yes. Six weeks. Have you been there before?"

"No. Never."

And, if truth be told, I really had no inclination to go there either: or anywhere else in the United States of America for that matter. It had always seemed to me to be a quite unappealing country filled with over-opinionated, overweight, overbearing people who were under the impression that their ancestors had fought to gain independence from Great Britain.

"What?" I hear you ask. "Surely the American War of Independence is an historical fact?"

Well, sort of. You see, the truth of the matter is that we – as a nation – were rather glad to see the back of the place. Now I realise that this version is seldom to be read in official history books, but I have it on good authority that George III said to

Frederick North (the then First Lord of the Treasury – now more commonly known as the Prime Minister. I believe Henry Campbell-Bannerman was the first to be officially known as the Prime Minister, and that was in 1905) that it might be a good idea to get rid of 'that damned tax-shirking colony', and that dear old inept Freddy was just the man to do it. Especially as 'that damned tax-shirking colony' wanted representation and was going to make friends with the French. I also believe that the Right Honourable F. North spat as he said the word 'French'.

I wish to make it clear that I have nothing much against the French. Au contraire. Why, every October 21st I choose a random telephone number in Paris (always a random one as I do not wish to have a charge of favouritism levelled against me) and I wish the person who answers my call a 'Happy Trafalgar Day'. I also let the recipient of my beneficence know that I am telephoning from Waterloo Station, and that I am wearing a pair of Wellington Boots. Yet, despite the obvious attempt at 'Bonhomie' on my part (note also my attempt at bilingual camaraderie), the recipient has never, to this day, thanked me for my display of goodwill.

In fact, I have yet to receive information to contradict my impression that the French have never bothered to officially say 'thank you' to the British for going to their assistance around 1914 and again in 1939. But I cannot herd all the French into the same enclosure, as there are many people of a French persuasion who respectfully attend to the graves of British soldiers who died whilst defending and liberating French soil. So, as one might again say, 'chapeaux off' to them.

Furthermore, just in case I churn out any critical remarks about the Belgians at some stage in this tome, I shall take this opportunity to make mention of the fact that at 8.00 pm every night since 1921, certain members of the Belgian Fire Brigade play the 'Last Post' at the Menin Gate in honour of the Allied dead from the First World War.

"So, does the prospect excite you?" Ms Forsopition enquired.

I was about to say "Not in the slightest" or "I would rather let Ray Charles carry out root-canal treatment on one of my molars", when I felt that a large slice of discretion was called for. "I would consider it to be a delight," was what actually passed my lips.

"Great. I'll start making all the necessary arrangements."

"Jolly good."

Several days were to pass before I next heard from Ms Forsopition. Several days that were to prove to be amongst the last sane ones that I was going to spend in the coming weeks.

Having said that, I realise that 'sanity' is a very subjective state of affairs. What passes for normal behaviour in one society may often be regarded as outrageous in another. We in the West – that mainstay of civilisation – would never contemplate leaving our homes without first making sure that Mr Mortice was in full employment. Yet, there are societies that regard the necessity to lock one's home as an indication that all is not well on the sophistication front.

However, to balance the argument slightly, we – of Occidental origins - don't think it awfully attractive, or even clever, to slap a wooden dinner plate in the middle of one's lower lip. It might be very handy if you are the sort of eater who doesn't always feel the necessity for using a knife and fork; but I would imagine it can be rather off-putting, and even injurious, if one has intentions in the osculation arena.

Mind you, there are sections of our own society that think it charismatic to stick various metal objects through various parts of their anatomy. Not objects in the household appliance territory, you understand, but I feel that day is not far off. I refer, of course, to the 'fad' of body piercing. I would have thought that 'body mutilation' or even 'body humiliation' might be more appropriate: but nobody ever takes the time to come and ask me for my views on the matter.

27

Whatever it is that possesses otherwise seemingly intelligent people to feel the need to push a piece of metal through a part of their body, escapes me. Although, I suppose, by definition, intelligent people probably don't feel this need. Or if they do, perhaps they don't quite have enough of the grey matter to realise that other members of society understand that the practice is usually reserved for those who have little to distinguish themselves from other members of the *Profanum Vulgus*.

I am not, incidentally, referring to ear-lobes. I think that some jewellery adorning this part of the body is acceptable: possibly even attractive. But shoving metal though noses, navels, and eyebrows is something which, in my opinion, is purely designed to allow other people to know in advance that they would be wasting their time if they tried to engage the owner of such facial fripperies in a meaningful dialogue.

As for those who feel the need to push metal through other, possibly softer, and usually well-hidden, parts of their anatomy ... Well, I shall refrain from passing comment! Apart from saying that tongue-piercing is the type of thing that can lead to cellular changes that one would rather do without. You only have to ask someone who knows about the effect that even a rough tooth can have on one's stylo-glossus and palato-glossus muscles. Seldom a pleasant end result, I can assure you.

Anyway, to return from my judgemental parenthesis, I soon I received another phone call.

"Mr Phalarope?"

"Yes."

"Hi ... it's Jocelyn Forsopition here."

"Oh, hello there, and a very good morning to you."

"Thank you. And how are you?"

"I'm very well, thank you. And I trust I find you in the rudest of rude."

"Excuse me?"

"Rudest of rude health. Hale and hearty."

"Er ... I'm doing just fine."

"Good."

Pleasantries exchanged, Ms Forsopition went on to say that we were to meet at a shopping centre the following morning.

"To what end?" I politely enquired.

"To revitalise your wardrobe."

I have to admit to not having, up to that moment, ever considered the vitality of my wardrobe: or my chest of drawers for that matter. They had both seemed, to someone who knows little of these matters, in particularly fine fettle when last I saw them, and more than happy with their current positions. Although, if pressed, I think the chest of drawers would have preferred a spot nearer the window. I pointed out this fact to Ms Forsopition. I recall that her reply was "What?"

"I was merely wondering why the vivaciousness of my bedroom furniture should be of any consequence."

"Your what?"

"My wardrobe."

"What about your wardrobe?"

"You said you wanted to revitalise it."

"I said what? Your ... No, I meant your *clothes*."

"Oh."

"But I can also advise on Feng Shui if you want."

"You can do what?"

"Tell you about Feng Shui."

Anyway, to circumvent a protracted discourse during which Ms Forsopition seemed determined to extol the virtues, and necessity, of Feng Shui, - particularly where bedroom furniture is concerned - I agreed to meet her at the appointed place and at the appointed hour.

In the meantime, I decided to find out what I could about Feng Shui: in case I was asked some searching and far-reaching questions. I found an article about the philosophy that creates an environment which is ergonomic, and allows one to work efficiently, comfortably and successfully by following the patterns of nature. Interesting, I thought, as I tried to imagine myself as a boat, and my house as a shirt. I even had a go at moving my furniture around. So much, in fact, that I, my wardrobe, my chest of drawers and a rather fetching standard lamp felt quite dizzy with it all.

I then tried my drinks cabinet facing East; I tried it facing West: I even had a dabble with it facing North for a while. I was, unfortunately, unable to sense any improvement in my spiritual wellbeing: and when I tried with the cabinet facing South, I found that I was unable to open it. However, as soon as I realised that Feng Shui actually means wind and water, I came to the conclusion that there is probably a very good reason for that.

Soon after, at the prescribed time, I was to be found standing outside a shop that purported to sell items of gentlemen's clothing. I say 'purported', as I didn't actually notice anything in the window – apart from a sign - that might lead a gentleman to understand that such items were, in fact, to be found for sale within said premises.

I believe I allowed several minutes to pass before I considered, as Ms Forsopition was nowhere to be seen, that she might already be inside. I summoned up the courage to venture within its portals, and no sooner had I done so than I began to feel distinctly light-headed and anxious not to add epilepsy to the list of ailments with which I have suffered over the years. Suffering, if my mother is to be believed, I have endured ever since the day – maybe even the moment – of my conception. Or did she say that I had *caused* the suffering?

I don't know if any of you have ever tried to negotiate your way around a shop that purveys items of clothing (although I believe any items will work just as well) with your eyes tightly shut in order to avoid any possibility of feeling a sudden desire to partake of a mal (whether petit or grand): if so, then you will understand the commotion that resulted.

I tried explaining my predicament to an extremely attractive young lady (who was either from Cardiff or Madras – I was unable to tell the shade of her skin in the somewhat dim lighting, and I have already mentioned my shortcomings in the accent-spotting department) but, I'm afraid to say, that I was unable to sound very coherent as I couldn't take my eyes off the name (at least I think it was a name) that was proudly displayed on her not inconsiderable bosom. But more of that later. By 'that', I mean both the bosom and the name.

I fear that I must have sounded, and probably appeared, like a cross between Norman Wisdom and someone on their way to have a lingual fraenectomy. I don't recall saying anything that might have been taken to cause offence, but in what seemed like only a few seconds, I found myself being escorted from the premises by a rather large man in a suit that was quite obviously on the tight side of comfortable for him.

I was just about to point out the fact that he might find some advantage in having a look at the selection of goods on sale – stroboscopic lighting not withstanding – in order to find a jacket that would surely have allowed him a good deal more freedom of movement, when Ms Forsopition came bursting onto the scene; spouting forth apologies for having kept me waiting.

"Do you know this man?" asked the suited gorilla.

"Yes. Why?" answered my sartorial director.

"'Cos he was causing a disturbance."

"Where?"

"In the shop."

"Were you?"

"No," I replied, feeling slightly affronted by her enquiry.

"The assistant said you was rude to 'er," growled the simian. "An' being sexually 'arassing. Staring suggestive-like at 'er breasts, and that."

"What!" Ms Forsopition exclaimed, giving me a most unsavoury glance.

"What!" I exclaimed, dispensing with what would have been a fully justified reciprocal glance in return.

"Were you staring ... suggestively ... at her breasts?"

31

"No I jolly well was not. I may have been focussing on her, um, chestal area for a moment; but I was merely trying to read what her name was." I turned back to the source of the tumult. "And then it was my intention to meet Miss Proposition here."

"What!" exclaimed the primate.

"What!" exclaimed Ms Forsopition.

"What?" I offered.

It took several moments for the unfortunate misunderstanding to be cleared up. I, being the perfect gentleman, took the time to explain to Ms Forsopition that I had not long arrived, but would have considered a wait of any length to be perfectly acceptable. I thought I noticed a slight glare in her eyes, possibly tinged with a hint of inflamed feminism; but it soon passed. Thankfully; as I have always felt it advisable to spend as short a time as possible caught between a Neanderthal and an Amazon: especially when they both have the scent of prey in their unsettlingly flaring nostrils.

I really have to give thanks at this point to my cousin Dick, who once spent an entire weekend dissuading me from entering the world of medicine in my quest to pursue a career as an ENT surgeon. I have no idea why the fancy to enter the well-trodden halls of Hippocrates should have entered my consciousness; and even less idea why I should have wanted to spend my working life perusing into areas that, nowadays, seem utterly revolting to me. Especially when I think of the number of children I have seen who have been determined to collect as much of the material that their nose produces with the intention of blowing it into bubbles through their nostrils: and to do so in a manner that would suggest they are enormously proud of this peculiar ability. In fact, the larger the bubble the prouder they become.

I have studied works by Socrates and Aristotle, as well as Gurdjieff and Freud, but I have been unable to discover any societal advantage to be gained by this talent. I have also delved through treatises written by Herbert Spencer and Jacob Bronowski and could find no mention, not even a hint, of any benefit to be achieved by being able to walk around with a green balloon protruding from your nose. In fact, my own observations have shown that people who possess, and display, this skill tend to be shunned by other members of their society: and quite rightly too.

As for the contents of the otic aperture ... Well, apart from being able to make flaccid candles, I can think of no use whatsoever for the detritus lurking therein. Although I have just remembered a boy from my prep school (Jonathon 'waxy' Thompkins) who was able to remove clods from his ear with a paper clip, attach them to the end of a flexible wooden ruler, then propel them across the classroom and make them stick to the wall. Impressive though that may have been, especially to a ten year-old, I really cannot think of any modern-day event where such behaviour might be considered an advantage. Unless, of course, they decide to make it an Olympic event. Whilst on the subject, I seem to remember an Australian politician who was once caught on camera eating his own ear wax; and I have a feeling that he went on to become Prime Minister. Perhaps there is a use for the ghastly stuff after all.

Then we have the throat; and I think that most people are aware of the sort of rubbish that emanates from that cavity for me not to elaborate further. So, all things considered, I really owe Dick my eternal gratitude. Maybe I should have tried to do the same for him, as he went on to become a proctologist.

So anyway, there I was, patiently waiting for Ms Forsopition's nostrils to return to a size that was less than adequate to allow for the easy parking of an average sized hatchback.

Normal dimensions eventually resumed, and my fear of being hoovered up from sight soon abated. Ms Forsopition slowly (and with rather too much of a sneer for my liking) looked me up and down, passed a comment about how wooden my clothing was and how I would have to update it in order to blend successfully with the average inhabitant of San Francisco.

Quite why the condition of my raiment should have any bearing on my ability to synthesize with people who dwelled within the boundaries of what was once known as Yerba Buena escaped me. I had to go and look up what that means, by the way: it translates as 'Good Herb', or 'Good Grass'. Hmm: I wonder if the city's antecedents knew something. I expect I shall never know. However, to return to the matter of outfits, if my hitherto impressions were anything to go by, I should have thought that my clothing – wooden or otherwise - would have had less influence on my ability to blend in with the occupants of San Francisco than a desire to wear a pink tutu and blow a whistle loudly whilst sashaying through the Castro District.

"Why?" I politely asked. "The clothes that I possess have provided me with sterling service over the years."

At that point Ms Forsopition gave a loud, and completely undisguised, snigger. "That, my dear Mr Phalarope, is precisely what I mean. You need some new clothes."

"Well," I continued. "I sincerely hope that you don't intend I look for any inside the emporium behind me." I believe that I may have used my thumb to point backwards over my shoulder whilst I spoke. "Indeed I do not."

"As a matter of fact, I do. Why?"

"Apart from having no desire to take Epanutin for the rest of my life, I didn't notice anything in there that caught my eye." Apart from, of course, the name of one of the shop assistants. I have no wish to appear ill-versed in the ways of other cultures (even though I usually do), but I would have thought that a woman having the word 'Shittal' embroidered upon her shirt front is not exactly going to bring out the best in her customers. Never mind how accurate it may be regarding the size of bosom upon which it has been positioned. I should put it on a par with having the name 'Elano' emblazoned across the seat of your trousers whilst selling items in a retail outlet in Madrid.

Yes, yes, I can hear all the paid-up members of the PC brigade bleating about how something or other 'ist' they think I am being. Well, I don't care. I, along with the vast majority of my indigenous compatriots, am not a polyglot; nor, as I recently mentioned, have I been overly exposed to what might well be commonplace names in other countries. When I see the word 'Shittal' on somebody's shirt front, my immediate reaction is one of astonishment: and, yes, I am probably going to stare a bit as well. Anyway, my conversation with Ms Forsopition continued.

"Did you look closely at anything?" she asked.

"Only at her bosom," I replied.

"What!"

"What?"

"You just said looked closely at her bosom. Whose bosom?"

"The young girl at the till."

"I consider that to be most inappropriate behaviour."

"I only wanted to make sure of what she had written on it."

"What! She had something written on it?"

"Indeed. Which I thought was most peculiar, especially as the breast in question seemed more than adequate to me."

"I beg your pardon!"

"Why?"

"What?"

"I have no idea where this is going, but I'm already lost."

For a moment, Ms Forsopition looked as though she wasn't sure whether to give me a slap or walk in front of a moving bus. I expect that even if I live to the grand old age of 120 I doubt if I shall ever quite understand the female psyche. Rum old creatures aren't they? But there we are: I expect the Creator meant well at the time.

"Did you look at the clothes?" she finally asked, composure regained.

"Yes," I lied, knowing full well that I had spent most of the time wandering around with my eyes closed.

"And ...?"

"Nothing else; just the clothes."

"No, I meant did you find anything that might be considered suitable?"

"Not exactly."

"Not exactly?"

"No. Actually, not even close."

"Oh. Are you sure?"

"Very."

"Pity."

"Indubitably. Might I be permitted," I asked, after what seemed like a suitable pause, "to enquire why I need to change my apparel?"

"Because the purpose of this whole piece is to equip you to spend six weeks in San Francisco; learning about how the city and its inhabitants function. And we at the magazine feel that this will be done best without you looking like a tourist."

"The 'whole piece'?"

"Yeah. The whole point of the competition."

"Which is ...? Do remind me." Actually, it wasn't really going to remind me as I hadn't known from the start.

"We are a new publication ..." *Which would partly account for the fact that I hadn't seen it.* "... that is looking for innovative features ..." *For 'innovative' read 'barmy'.* "... to get our readership ..." *Currently hovering around fourteen people I've no doubt.* "... to take a wider interest in people from other parts of the world."

"Oh. Ah."

"And it was decided that sending someone to live in San Francisco for six weeks – someone who had never been there before ... You did say that you had never been there before, didn't you?"

"I did indeed."

36

"... would be a really great way of promoting trans-global understanding."

I remember thinking at the time that, considering the number of immigrants one happens across in our once great capital, trans-pavement understanding would have made more sense as a place to begin. However.

For the next two hours, Jocelyn (the more observant amongst you may have noticed that I am now using Ms Forsopition's Christian name – I felt that our cordiality was sufficient to allow same) and I traipsed around several places that peddled men's clothing. I use the word 'places' as I was unsure if some of the shops we entered were nightclubs, bordellos, or simply somewhere that people with limited use of eyes and ears had stumbled into, and out of which they had been unable to find their way.

Finally, after much debate, and possibly a hint of argument, a range of new clothing was obtained that was mutually deemed suitable for the trip ahead. And, by coincidence, the garments bore a very close resemblance to the clothes that I already possessed. Now, I am unsure whether this outcome was because I am fairly resolute in my choice of apparel, or because Jocelyn finally came round to my way of thinking. I fear that a certain Ray Davies would have received little inspiration for his song from my direction.

Amongst other things, I am the sort of chap who likes to tuck his shirt into his trousers. Not for me the rather peculiar habit of having the ends of your shirt dangling in a most dishevelled manner – as if you had lost the instructions on how to don said item. As for the quite peculiar notion of wearing 'two casual with one smart' item of clothing ... Again, least said and so forth.

But it matters not: my outfits were duly chosen and paid for: and for about one third of the price that Jocelyn's employers had estimated; and, on the acknowledgement that an impressive sum of currency had been saved, it was unanimously decided, after

37

a short consultation, that a taxi-ride and a jolly good meal were in order.

Jocelyn and I then discovered that there was something else about which we had absolutely nothing in common. Jocelyn was something of a lentil-lover, whilst I am rather prone to pounding my premolars on victuals of a more animal-type origin: specifically those parts that once possessed a contractile function.

I have to confess to never having been one with a desire for getting on the outside of visceral commodities; and I also draw the line at liver, kidney, heart, and those muscles that once belonged in the mouth. My reasoning is not on any grounds of taste, in the flavour department that is, but more on the grounds of not wanting some animal's tongue endeavouring to appeal to my own: especially when one considers the sort of places into which it might have ventured during its working life.

As for organs of sight or reproduction ... Well, I don't think there is enough space in this book for all my denunciations.

I also lack the ability to find allure with game: there is something about the likes of duck, pheasant and rabbit that I find quite unpalatable. Not too keen on veal or venison either. However, wave a bacon sandwich or a plateful of roast lamb under my olfactory organ, and my ptyalin production shifts into overdrive.

So, while Jocelyn struggled with her nut cutlet (or whatever it was), I tucked into one of the best 10oz sirloins I had eaten for a long while. And before I hear wails of anguish from any plant-pushers, I shall add – by way of amelioration – that the meat was 'well done'. There is something about food that bleeds, winces, or flaps across my plate when I stick a fork into it that I find rather off-putting. But that's me.

During said meal, I engaged Jocelyn in a discussion about the way that so many people are led, as if by a ring through their noses, into buying clothes that are quite obviously unsuitable to them. When will the populace come to realise that the only reason fashions change is because the manufacturers need to talk people into replacing their clothes with a regularity that exceeds the one determined by a natural wear and tear process?

"Ooh," they cry, "this year's fashion is now in the shops, so I had better go and part with some of my hard-earned cash and help keep the clothing industry moguls in the life of luxury to which they have become accustomed."

I am sure that I should cry as well if it was my money that was dwindling in such a vain and worthless pursuit of public approbation.

For my part, I have always held with the maxim that I shall only buy clothes that suit me – as far as my character and physical shape are concerned - rather than because it has suddenly become all the rage. Two benefits are to be gained from this approach. Firstly, I do not have to part with substantial sums of ill-afforded capital; and secondly, nobody is able to date any of the photographs in which I happen to make an appearance.

As a result of the latter motive, there are no photographic records that can elicit derogatory comments about flared trousers, kipper ties, tank tops, drainpipes, or any such similar catastrophes of a coutural nature on my part. The same, I hasten to add, can also be said about my hair.

I have been blessed with hair that has been determined not to fall out and, as a result, it has not been necessary to alter my coiffure over the years. I think I was about sixteen years old when it became apparent what style of hair presentation would best suit me, and I have adopted that mode ever since.

"How boring", some have said. I have even heard the term 'unimaginative' used. Well, boring and unimaginative it might be, but capable of giving rise to bouts of raucous laughter from peripatetic photograph perusers it is not: and that is the way I would prefer it to stay. In fact, if, for some reason, a photograph is taken of me shortly before the time that has been chosen for me to hand in my Earthly notice, I am sure people will comment that my hair looks just the same as it did when I was sixteen.

Unless, of course, I happen to depart this life whilst standing outside in a force ten gale.

However, I have to admit that said barnet is showing one or two areas that might answer to the description of 'greying'. But, as I have sometimes heard said, there is nothing wrong with grey hair ... ask anyone who is bald. And the grey, if I may say so myself, does add a certain distinction to my overall bearing.

Granted my face, and possibly a large percentage of the rest of my body, will alter as the years fade from my account – when in eternal lines to time I grow'st - but my hair will be combed in exactly the same style: or at least it had better be. It will be just my luck that death will have visited itself upon me at the same time that the aforementioned dizygotic (or fraternal if you prefer) issue of my sister have qualified from embalming college, and are anxiously seeking an opportunity of putting their skills to the test. I wouldn't put it past them to leave the final arrangement of my hair in a style more befitting someone with Mohican ancestry.

If they do, I shall consider it my duty to return – in spirit form – and frighten every ounce of the proverbial out of them on as regular a basis as I can manage.

A little later, while Jocelyn and I were enjoying our coffees, we happened to confabulate about the format that my sojourn to San Francisco was likely to take. I asked if she was going to be accompanying me, to which she replied - in a manner that seemed a little too effusive for my liking - "No."

I was going to be met at the airport (San Francisco International Airport – known as SFO for short) by a representative from the burgeoning USA branch of the publication; and was going to be staying, not in an expensive (or even moderately rated) hotel, but in an apartment belonging to a close friend of the one of the British editors. A boardroom discussion had decided that an apartment would allow me to get closer to the San Francisco populace than staying in an impersonal hotel room. Made sense, I supposed.

I am not a seasoned traveller as far as aircraft are concerned: not of late, anyway. I believe that my first journey by air-borne travel was at the tender age of two months, in a Constellation – or maybe it was a Viscount – that was flying from Colombo to Heathrow: and that was more years ago than I care to remind myself. My second flight was made a few months later, possibly in the same type of aeroplane – it would certainly have been one that was propeller driven – only, on the second occasion, it would have been flying from Heathrow back to Colombo.

Obviously my memories of flying at that age are a little blurry. Not because my intellectual powers, especially those concerned with memory, are of a flawed nature. Indeed not: in fact my earliest memory is that of being held upside down, slapped rather hard on my sitting regions, and hearing a loud voice declare, "It's a boy!"

No, I think the reason, at least I'm fairly certain it's the cause, is that my mother used to keep my head covered with a blanket during the flights. Why? I'm not sure. I wasn't aware that BOAC had a policy regarding the physical attractiveness of its cabin crew in those days; so the fear of a small boy being upset by a singularly unpleasant-looking air-stewardess who was (possibly) in need of a shave can, I feel sure, be dismissed. On top of which, I am fairly certain that in those days the qualifying criteria to become a member of the team were a good deal harder to fulfil than presently. But there again, perhaps it was the fear of upsetting the cabin crew by exposing them to a singularly unattractive infant that was uppermost in my mother's mind. I wonder if Michael Jackson heard about it.

I'm not aware of any similar problems that were encountered when we went out East by ship. Names such as Staffordshire (which I believe belonged to the Bibby Line and sailed out of Liverpool), Arcadia and Corfu spring to mind: as does a rather amusing tale of my mother's attempts to circumvent the rather strict customs officials who frequented the port of Colombo in those days.

It was the practice of my grandmother to send items out to us in Ceylon – usually in the company of a family friend who happened to be travelling in that direction – and my mother, not wishing to pay import duty when said items arrived would go on board the ship to collect them. The main problem encountered was how to make it look, when disembarking, as though she already those items in her possession when she boarded.

Many is the time I have been regaled by the story of how, on one occasion, she walked back down the gangplank with my new potty on her head so as to look like a hat.

Needless to say, not after it had been used for the purpose for which it had originally been designed. I somehow doubt, under those conditions, the immigration officials would have been fooled. Possibly dissuaded from taking the matter any further, but not fooled.

Anyway, I returned to my cottage, with my new clothes, and awaited instruction regarding the next phase of my adventures.

At the Airport.

The third Friday of September found me walking though the entrance to Terminal 1 of Heathrow Airport, at six-thirty in the morning. Not exactly an hour at which I am usually wide-awake, or in the mood to entertain passers-by with my wit and repartee. Although it has to be said that even though I am not always fully cognisant of my immediate environs or firing on all cylinders, I am generally in a better mood during the earlier hours of the day. Quite why, I have never been certain: perhaps it is a trait that I inherited from my father. But there again, come to think of it, he always had a kind word to say to people and was fairly amenable whatever the hour: brought about, I should imagine, by his many years of active service in the Merchant Navy. Or should that be, for the purists amongst you, the Merchant Service?

Anyway, there I was, dull-eyed and sparsely-tailed, wandering in through the automatic doors, and nearly collapsing under the weight of an over-filled case.

"Why didn't you use a case with wheels on?" I hear some of you ask.

"What sort?" I politely reply. "I trust that you don't mean one of those ghastly things with an extending handle."

"Why not? They are extremely useful."

"Never. Those, I feel, have been designed for persons of a certain age and temperament."

"Eh?" I hear you mutter.

By my, presumably sweeping, statement, I mean that they usually belong to the group of people who leave their supermarket trolleys stationed at right-angles to the shelf, and slap bang in the middle of the aisle, while they come to a decision about what next to place in it. Or they stop in the entrance of the supermarket in order to check their receipt, or look for their car keys, or say "hello" to someone they know. In other words, people who have absolutely no sense of space or the relationship of objects within said space. That, I am sure you will agree, is a smidgen on the irritating side when they are in command of a shopping trolley; but borders on the terrifying when you then see them then get behind the wheel of a car and drive away.

So, because being lumped in with such individuals is not very high on my agenda, I prefer to struggle on gallantly; even though I know that if continue doing so for too long I may well end up with one of my clavicles running horizontally (as Nature intended) whilst the other one points straight at the ground. This arrangement might be thought attractive, or even clever, in some social circles, but would be a confounded nuisance when getting measured for a suit.

Speaking of suits, have you noticed the dearth of bespoke tailors these days? The sort of response I normally receive when I enquire about getting a new suit is ...

"Made to measure, sir? What's that? We have a very nice range of 'mix-and-match'."

Mix and match! I didn't go there to buy a bag of sweets. It would seem that, as with many other facets of our life, the controlling powers would have us all pushed into convenient (and, therefore, easy to manage) compartments. The extinction of individualism is gathering apace.

Anyway, my flight wasn't due to leave until eleven that morning, and the material that came with my ticket said that I should check in around two to three hours before take-off.

"But hang on," I hear the more observant among you say, "Weren't you a tad early?"

Why, yes I was: and the reason for that is due to seventy-five and a quarter inches of elevation: and that is without shoes. I am, by nature and appearance, a tall man. Six feet three and a quarter inches to be precise: and that, as already proclaimed, is without shoes – which can add up to a further inch in my case. But not, I am happy to say, any more, as I am not prone to wearing footwear with high-heels.

Whilst – especially given the shape of my arches – I may well look rather fetching in a pair of sling-backs, asymmetric or otherwise, I am happy to say that my natural proclivities have never drawn me in that direction. However, I would like to make it clear that I do not wish to make any disparaging remarks about men who have a yearning towards wearing clothes of a feminine disposition; and, believe you me, there are plenty such remarks from which I could choose. A very odd state of affairs, all the same. I'm not sure whether I have any firmly fixed views on the matter, apart from thinking it must be extremely inconvenient if, as a fully-paid up member of the male side of the species, your natural urges involve getting togged up in a little black, off-the-shoulder number.

I have read several articles on the subject of people who feel trapped inside someone else's body: and, come to think of it, one or two about people who have literally been trapped therein.

I seem to recall the name for one such condition was a word that ended in 'ismus', and was a derivation of the Latin word for 'sheath'. My sense of propriety forbids me from going into further detail, except just to say that the whole matter must be rather disconcerting: and equally difficult from which to attract help. Mind you, I expect that there are many worse places in which to be trapped.

Before I leave the subject of dressing, a very good friend of mine, who had better remain nameless, once confided in me about a penchant of his for walking around his domicile wearing shoes that would ordinarily be seen loitering below nicely-turned lower legs and shapely ankles - such as those commonly found belonging to the gender that is equipped for child-bearing - rather than below a pair of gastrocnemius muscles that would not have looked out of place on a rugby prop forward.

"How do you know that?" you ask.

Because I had seen those same muscles on many a winter's Saturday afternoon as I knelt down with my arm tightly grasping my fellow member of the second row. I shall not elaborate any further - particularly as to whether the calf muscles belonged to the tight or loose head prop for fear of revealing the identity of the owner of the calf muscles in question.

My (probably now erstwhile) good friend went on to tell me that although he had mastered the art of perambulating in a straight line, he still had a great deal of difficulty in negotiating sharp corners and using stairs: particularly if the dress he was wearing was a bit on the tight side. From that day I was never able to bind correctly without wondering if I was going to find myself grabbing hold of a suspender belt instead of the robust crutch of a pair of rugby shorts.

But back to the lofty item under discussion, and my early arrival at the check-in desk. I had taken the trouble to read my ticket for an indication of the time that the flight would take – allowing for turbulence and being held up behind planes towing caravans – and discovered that something in the region of ten hours would elapse between leaving Heathrow and arriving at San Francisco International Airport.

I have occasionally felt able (but not altogether happy) to spend two or three hours with my knees up round my ears (on flights to and from the near continent – and once in a car from Rhydybeddhau to Bedwellty), but the thought of remaining in the 'praying mantis' position (or something similar) for ten hours filled me with the same amount of joie de vivre as I might display if I happened to notice four men on rather apocalyptic-looking horses cantering in my direction.

So I decided to arrive in plenty of time, in order to secure myself a seat with adequate leg-room to a) maintain sufficient circulation in my lower extremities to confidently cross gangrene off the list of impediments that I might develop during the flight, and b) be able to walk though American customs without giving the impression that I had received a personal type of injury brought about by the powerful suction mechanism operating in one of the aeroplane's toilets.

Two very reasonable and, I had hoped, very easily accommodated fears of mine. So, four hours ahead of schedule, I presented myself at the appropriate desk, with the intention of successfully carrying out the aforementioned objective. Unfortunately I found myself in a situation that reminded me of a set of criteria that I would like to see employed before political parties choose their prospective candidates. Although, to be honest, I should rather like to see it used whenever anybody is being selected for a position that involves making decisions about other people's lives.

"Which is?" I hear you ask.

Rather a long list, actually, but the one uppermost at the time was that concerning height. I have long since held the view – initially brought about from careful observation of the type of individual most likely to put forward their name to be in charge of a school society – that short males are not to be trusted. Yes, there are some perfectly amenable men who can only lean on the bar of a public house by first procuring the services of a wooden box: and yes, Winston Churchill could hardly have been described as gangly. However, in my eyes, short men do tend to lug around a rather extensive array of chips and complexes; and I, for one, would rather not see such individuals in positions where they feel compelled and, possibly more importantly, able to make up for lost ground: so to speak.

Let us elect a chap of equanimity every time.

Anyway, I believe the conversation that I had with the gentleman of Lilliputian stature (presumably on some sort of day-release scheme from his isle of birth) behind the check-in desk went something like ...

"Yes sir?" he said, as I approached.

"Hello. I'm booked on the 11.00 am flight to San Francisco."

"Do you have a ticket?"

"Yes," I replied, thinking that the answer should have been fairly obvious. Unless, of course, the gentleman with the soon-to-be-displayed Hitler complex thought I resembled the type of person who was in the habit of making false claims.

"How many pieces of luggage have you got?"

Now I have to admit to being caught on the hop with that question; and needed to pause while I mentally rummaged through my attic, clearing away the old cobwebs and dustsheets. "Twelve, if my memory serves me correctly."

"What!"

"Twelve," I repeated, wondering if my habit of hanging on to valises was in someway unusual.

"Where?"

"At home, in my attic. Well, ten of them are. The remainder are here with me now."

The homunculus then began showing me a selection from his obviously extensive repertoire of facial expressions and hissing noises. "How many items of luggage are you intending to take onto the plane?" he finally managed to say.

"Two," I replied, quickly deciding that the fellow wasn't up to speed in the mental arithmetic department.

"Right. And did you pack your cases yourself?"

You will be pleased to hear I did not answer that question by making any glib reference to having got my butler, a small group of Filipino women, or a shifty-looking gentleman of Middle Eastern appearance who answered to the name of Osama, to pack for me. I wanted to, but I felt that a full-body search followed by several days being held at her Majesty's pleasure would not get my foray to California off to the best start.

"Yes," I replied, barely managing to keep a straight face.

I really was behaving myself. There is so much scope for jesting that I found myself wondering how people ever manage to reach their allotted aircraft without succumbing to the pleasures that can be enjoyed through merry badinage with certain members of the airport staff. And when you are confronted with one of said members who is at least twelve inches below the height that would normally make you stop and think about possible physical repercussions, then it really does take a steely type of will to desist from partaking of some gentle ribaldry.

Fortunately, even though I say it myself, I am in possession of a resolve upon whose constitution Titanium was originally based. Not all of the time, I must admit, but generally when needs must. Unless I decide otherwise: and that is usually when the trouble starts. Imagine the contortions that might arise when trying to control iron steadfastness with a steely determination. Not even Plato was presented with such a conundrum. Which is probably just as well, as his philosophy rejected scientific rationalism in favour of arguments. Although, thinking about the metallic element to the problem of my will, Plato did enjoy trapping his students by getting them to contradict themselves with examples such as 'Iron' on poetry.

Now, in case you are expecting me to expand on the dilemma that Plato both constructed and avoided, I shall make it clear that I have no intention of doing so: for two very good reasons. The first is that there are not enough pages in this book to contain all the words necessary to fully explain his philosophy. Secondly, and probably more germane, is that I have little or no idea what he was going on about. Anyway, it was Plato who correctly identified the harmful, drug-like, ephemeral effect of great thinkers.

Whilst on the subject of Plato, did you know his real name was Aristocles, and Plato was the nickname he got because of his wide shoulders? No? Nor did I until quite recently. Anyway.

Even Ecclesiastes enters the discussion with fourpence worth of ponderance when it mentions a bit about 'He that increaseth knowledge increaseth sorrow'. I expect that's why I'm usually quite a cheerful sort of fellow.

"Have you left them unattended for any time since you arrived here?"

"No," I replied.

"Has anyone put anything inside them without your knowledge?"

It was at that point one of my eyebrows decided to elevate itself, and my mouth adopted a little smile. "Oh, that's very good," I said.

"What is?"

"Your question. Nearly caught me out." I believe I may have waggled my right index finger at the fellow as I spoke.

"What?"

"Is it some kind of airline 'in' joke?"

"What 'in' joke?"

"The one concerning the paradoxical nature of your last enquiry."

"The *what?*"

"The illogicality of asking me if I know whether or not there is something inside my case that I don't know about."

I now found myself caught between wanting to find out how dark a red colour the man's face could go before it burst and not wanting to detain the people behind me in the queue. I chose the judicious option.

"The answer to your question is no," I hurriedly said.

There was a brief pause as the man ran a finger around the inside of his collar, and I thought I detected some vapour escape through the gap.

After a slow, deep, breath he then said "Will you put the large one on the scale here."

"Certainly."

I can quite easily understand an aircraft company has to make sure the passengers intending to use the services they provide do not turn up with metal trunks that weigh in excess of several hundredweight, and that it has to weigh each piece in order to check that this is so: or else, presumably, the aircraft in question would verily struggle to get off the ground.

But what I do not understand is why some check-in weighing machine operator (usually wearing a uniform that patently does not suit them – either in style, size or colour) proceeds to tut-tut when one of the cases placed upon his scales weighs a couple of ounces more than the prescribed limit. Especially when he can quite clearly see that the next person in line – who is usually sneering in a knowing fashion – weighs several stones more than the previous ten cases added together.

Why can't airlines make allowances for persons of a lithe disposition - such as myself, for example - and give them some leeway regarding the weight of their belongings? I should have thought that someone of slender dimensions (and well within the height to weight guidelines as laid down by nearly all the

51

foremost medical authorities) with a suitcase that weighs eight pounds, for instance, more than the forty-four allowed, would cause less of a problem regarding the aircraft's struggles to become airborne than a person who weighs in at twice the recommended weight for his or her (and usually anyone else's as well) height.

A chap weighing in at 180 lbs who has a case that tips the scales at 60 lbs is, surely, going to be less of a burden on the engines than someone with a case of 44 lbs who personally stops the pointer at 280 lbs.

I hope you have noticed that I refer to weight in Imperial units. Not for me the horrible system that successive governments have subversively been trying to foist upon the British public. *Kilograms*! *Litres*! Absolutely deplorable. And how boring the metric dimensions are when compared to the wonderful array to be found within the Imperial compass?

Think of inches, feet, yards and miles and you conjure up scenes of long established systems that have served Englishmen well for countless centuries. Poles, chains and furlongs ... wonderful images of ploughs, cricket pitches and horse racing.

52

With metres I get images of French people - often short, with a hand tucked inside a waistcoat, and slightly deficient in the genital department - and those, I can assure you, are not images conducive to a contented existence.

Then we have liquids that are measured by the pint, the quart, and the gallon: maybe even a peck or two. I try not to dwell too long on the firkin (9 gallons or ¼ of a barrel), as I do not think I could prevent myself from feeling embarrassed should I ever have occasion to order one. And, not being much of a wine drinker, I should seldom have the opportunity to use terms such as runlet, tierce, hogshead or puncheon. Although, thinking about it, I may well take up subscription to the Bacchus appreciation approach to Life purely in order to use such terms. Indeed, I think that a life involving such measures would be infinitely more appealing than one dealing in units of the metric persuasion.

Whilst I am on the subject of glasses of wine, how on earth do those people – usually women, it has to be said - who down several glasses of some ghastly Chardonnay each evening manage to go to work the following morning? Especially when you can often easily substitute 'bucket' for 'glass'! Still, I suppose the ever-rising liver disease statistics have to be maintained.

But none of that, I fear, was going to impress the vertically challenged individual who faced me.

"And what about your carry on?" he then asked.

"What carry on? I was under the impression that I have been behaving myself in a perfectly acceptable manner."

"What?"

"I beg your pardon."

"What - Do you have a case that you want to *carry on* to the plane?"

"Oh. Right. Er, yes, Indeed I do," I said, unhooking the rucksack from my shoulders. I thought such items were known as hand-luggage: but there we are.

And there's an oft misunderstood term – 'hand-luggage'. I have always assumed that the item of luggage one is permitted to take on to the airplane should be of a size that can easily be placed in the overhead compartment. Years ago, passengers had to have a bag small enough to easily fit under their seat. Actually, I still have one of those same small suitcases - with an Air India logo on it - that fulfils the criterion.

These days, however, some people seem to think that hand-luggage is defined as no more than three or four items, or one that requires no more than three people to carry it through the departure lounge, and thence onto the plane. Those same three people are then needed to lift said item six feet off the ground and push it (sometimes with sufficient force to break objects in the adjacent cases) into the space provided above the seats. The process then has to be repeated, in reverse, upon arrival at the destination.

Also, I further ask, why do those same people always feel the need to stand up before the aircraft has stopped (or should that be 'moored'?) alongside the terminal, struggle to get their bags out of the overhead locker – usually dropping it onto the head of some poor unfortunate underneath – and then stand in the aisle, in a bunch, for a further ten minutes? Very odd.

"Okay," my pocket-sized panjandrum continued.

"Thank you."

"And just listen out for your flight to be called."

"Right. Oh ..." I said, suddenly remembering the purpose of my early visit.

"Yes ...?"

"My seat. I should like to have one by a door, please."

"Because ...?"

"Because ..." I felt slightly hesitant to mention my abundance of vertical inches when facing a man to whom Nature had not been quite so generous. "... because I have circulatory problems in my lower extremities, and I need to have my legs extended in order to avoid thromboses of the deep vein variety."

While inwardly feeling extremely pleased with my spontaneous inventiveness, I did, nevertheless, manage to restrain my desire to beam like the feline from Cheshire about which Charles Lutwidge Dodgson once wrote (there's more about him later, by the way) – under the nom de plume of Lewis Carroll. I also suppressed an urge to make mention of how this was a problem of which individuals with a dearth of inches between groin and ankle would know little.

It is a strange affliction that I have had to endure since I reached the age of about eighteen – and the aforementioned height of six feet, three and a quarter inches – that sometimes compels me to draw attention to the stately nature of my construction when compared with, say, someone who might accurately, albeit unkindly, be described as 'stumpy'.

Now I am the first to admit that not one inch of my vertical dimension is due, in any way, to anything that I may have contributed. Indeed, many of my teenage years were probably spent indulging in behaviour that might well have created a barrier to extending my height. Or was it supposed to cause blindness? I forget.

Neither, I must add, have any of those cursed with restricted growth been responsible for their personal altitude. Unless, of course, they have been known to indulge in the sort of body-binding practices normally reserved for the feet of certain Chinese women; or come from a family who, rather than shake hands, prefer to vigorously pat each other on the head.

"How old are you?"

"I beg your pardon," I replied, failing to see what my age had to do with anything relating to my ability to sit down without having to display the sort of flexibility normally only spotted in people who have assumed the prefix 'Yogi'. Except, perhaps, counting against it.

"How old are you?"

"Forty-nine. Why?"

"Because we prefer to have younger passengers near the emergency exits."

"And why is that?"

"In case of an emergency landing. They'll be able to get out faster than older passengers."

"And on what premise are you basing that conclusion?"

"Eh?"

"Why will younger people be able to vacate an aeroplane faster than older people."

"Younger people are more mobile."

"My dear sir ..." At this point I felt compelled to draw myself up to my full height (I may even have stood slightly on tip-toe to accentuate same) "... should an aircraft such as one designed to fly across an ocean and a continent find it necessary to cut short its journey before reaching an airport, I should imagine that, due to the force of impacting upon the ground at speeds in excess of two or three hundred miles an hour (I knew that the cruising speed of the aircraft would be over five hundred miles an hour, but I had assumed that the pilot would make a bit of an effort to slow down somewhat before resuming contact with terra firma), most of the passengers would find themselves in a rather compacted group at the front end of the fuselage, or scattered in a fairly higgledy-piggledy fashion across many acres of the Earth's surface. I very much doubt that they would be in the process of forming an orderly queue to disembark."

"What if it crashes at sea? Eh? What then?"

"Then you may substitute the word 'water' for the word 'ground'. I believe that water offers the same sort of welcome as concrete when visited from a great height."

"Er ... um ... What about if a fire breaks out before take-off? Hmm?"

"Then I should imagine that persons whose nature could best be described as sang-froid should be hovering near the top of the list of 'those best suited' for the job of helping others disembark. And, I can assure you, sir, that my sang is about as froid as it gets."

"Your ... But ..."

"No 'buts'. I am the first in line, and I want a seat by a door."

There then followed a short, but decisive, silence, and I knew I had procured the moral high ground.

"Right. There. Huh."

"Thank you," I replied, maintaining an air of magnanimity before, with a cheery wave, I set off to have a little something to eat.

At this point I ought to mention that when I say a 'little something', I really do mean a *little* something. I am not, by nature or inclination, someone who could accurately be described as a 'good traveller'. I even think the term 'moderate traveller' might surpass my normal capabilities. 'Bloody awful' is probably closest.

Not that I travel badly with every mode of transport. I do not recall ever emptying the contents of my stomach whilst cycling, or on horseback; but there are two rather pertinent reasons for that. Firstly, cycling – especially on uphill sections – requires one's concentration to be focussed on balance and the expenditure of energy. Both of those seem to draw my mind away from any likelihood of displaying a phenomenon known as reverse peristalsis. Secondly, horse riding fills me with such a degree of fear that any possibility of gastrointestinal movement would be mainly concentrated at the other end of my alimentary canal.

Thus, ever since early adulthood, I have endeavoured to have as little in the way of partly-digested comestibles within the confines of my gastric area whenever I embark upon travel. But, bearing in mind that most food starts leaving the stomach for the area known as the duodenum after three or so hours, and as there were still four hours until take-off, I felt able to partake of a little circumspect activity in the consuming sphere. So I headed towards the cafeteria area.

Speaking of which, I am, I have to say, at a bit of a loss as to why airports have food on offer that has, as one of its main ingredients, that rather odorous relative of the onion – namely, the garlic. Do the catering managers not realise the fetor that little bulb produces? A fetor that, incidentally, the likes of my good self can perceive from distances of up to a quarter of a mile in the open air: never mind from a few yards within the confines of a pressurised metal container. All you need is for one or two individuals among the passengers to have had something like Chicken Kiev and within minutes of take-off the whole aircraft smells like the Isthmus of Fauces belonging to a Frenchman whose oral hygiene is put to shame when compared with that shown by a hippopotamus. I realise that doesn't exactly narrow down the field, but there you are. Mephitic in the extreme.

On top of which, since the 'No Smoking' rule started, the air in the planes is merely re-circulated – rather than replaced – so the same old stuff keeps going round and round. Perhaps it might be more salubrious to allow passengers to light up again!

Also, I don't like the fact that the chemist shops in the airport sell those tablets that are purported to help one release trapped wind: especially if said tablets begin to work once the aircraft is in the air. I have always felt that such wind should remain well and truly trapped: or at least until there is nobody close enough to be aware of its release.

On the Plane

As I believe I have already mentioned, I have flown on many occasions, and I really ought to be totally at ease with the concept of a vehicle that is nearly 230 feet long, 200 feet from wing-tip to wing-tip, weighs in at 900,000 pounds, and with around 500 people inside is able to get off the ground when it reaches a particular speed. But I am not: even bearing in mind that it has the use of its two horizontal appendages sticking out: one on either side, of course.

For that I shall always extend my thanks to History for allowing flight to have been pioneered by Sir George Cayley, and not Pablo Picasso - regardless of whether it would have been during his 'Blue' or 'Rose' periods. I have just received a mental image of Messrs Alcock, Whitten-Brown and Bleriot attempting their stupendous flights in planes that had both wings sprouting from the same side. I think that the term 'groundbreaking' would have been aptly applied - in both a literal and a metaphorical sense.

However, back to the shuddering hulk in which I found myself. The behemoth was shortly, under the guidance and (I hoped) total control of its captain and crew, going to rumble down a designated concrete strip. Then, by the appropriate alteration of elevators, ailerons and flaps (combined with speed) the airflow above the wings is going to increase until lift exceeds weight and the aeroplane gets off the ground. I am also under the impression that two other factors – known as thrust and drag – play a part in the whole process. But to me, man-made flight will always have a final ingredient that plays the most important part of all: Magic.

I think you will find this ingredient plays a pivotal role in other facets of our present-day lives: television, CDs, DVDs, computers and mobile phones to name but five.

"But," I hear you cry, "I know how to use a computer."

I'm quite sure you do. But there is a fundamental difference between knowing how to use a computer, and knowing how it works. Can you explain to me *how* information is stored on a hard drive? Hmm? No, of course you can't: unless, that is, you use the term 'Magic'. I rest my case.

More intriguing is when I consider how just how advanced the capabilities of the hardware have become compared to the state of play of the operating software. Make you wonder if they both originated on the same planet. Anyway.

Then I heard the voice of a gentleman who introduced himself as 'Captain Wilkins'. He sounded a pleasant enough fellow, so I felt a good deal more relaxed than the time I heard the captain of one particular aircraft trying to introduce himself. I use the term 'trying' as it seemed that the poor individual concerned suffered from a stammer.

I shall take this opportunity to point out that I have nothing against people who suffer from that strange – and often debilitating – condition (more frequently seen in men than in women: as is colour-blindness, as a matter of interest. I believe it has something to do with a recessive gene that isn't counterbalanced because of the nature of the shape of the 'Y' chromosome). In fact, I have a great deal of both sympathy and empathy as I have to been known, on occasion, to have trouble in extricating a particular consonant from the recesses of my own oropharynx. But not, I hasten to add, whilst trying to allay the fears of several hundred fee-paying passengers. There is something ever so slightly disconcerting about hearing your captain for the flight describing himself as "Captain De-ve-de-ve-de-ve-deveno-deveni-na-nani-nish-shsh-devenish."

But I think even my unnerving incident pales into insignificance when compared to the situation experienced by a very good friend of mine – Keith Harruphe – who once told me of a trip he was making from Bembridge (on the Isle of Wight ... strange that we should both have had a disagreeable episode in the same place) when, sitting in the back of a light aeroplane (a

60

Cessna of some description I seem to recall, although Keith was a bit vague as he was suffering from some kind of delayed, post-traumatic amnesia) he watched as a man with whom he had, not half an hour before, been sharing a bottle of rather good Merlot, climbing into one of the front seats and claiming to be the pilot and that it was his intention to fly the assembled group to Biggin Hill.

I would rather not repeat the selection of expletives that Keith used whilst hurriedly disembarking from the flying machine and suggesting — in the strongest possible terms — that his fellow passengers had better do likewise; but I shall go as far as to say that his profanities were fully justified: even if they did call into question the marital and evolutionary status of the pilot's progenitors.

So there I was, as usual, tensely gripping the arms of my seat whilst the metal leviathan thundered down the runway. So tensely, in fact, that it seemed my knuckles would tear through my skin and soak me in blood. At least that is what might have happened, had it not been for the fact that I had fastened my lap-belt so tightly that blood was no longer circulating to all parts of my body: and I don't think I had managed to draw in breath for several minutes.

I may be mistaken, but I sometimes wonder if William E. Boeing had a slightly sadistic streak inside him. Did he foresee that such as I would one day be strapped inside a brainchild of his; quivering and shaking as the beast quivered and shook before steeling itself into taking off? I have a feeling that may be the case.

As I have mentioned, I am vaguely aware of the physics involved in the process of leaving the ground - I don't profess to understand it, merely that I have read about it - but I still find the whole thing utterly amazing. I looked out of the window, holding my breath (not that I had, as I also mentioned, all that much choice) with child-like wonder. I experienced that feeling of awe as, with barely more than a sigh and a small bounce, the wheels left the ground, and our journey into the sky began.

I then experienced feelings of nausea and earache as the aeroplane tilted upwards at an angle that suggested the pilot was having a 'bit of a laugh' whilst sucking away on a large bag of barley-sugars. Not for him the increasing differential in air-pressure between his middle ear and the rest of the cabin; and no squeaking Eustachian tubes either. Just a smugness that comes of knowing his passengers are now completely absorbed in holding their noses whilst trying to swallow. I expect he only wears his earphones to keep out the barrage of 'pops' that can probably be heard back in the control tower. However.

Several 'bings' and 'bongs' later, I was aware that the aircraft had practically levelled out, and was also fairly certain that the contents of my sinuses were not going to burst out through my ear-drums and all over the passengers sitting next to me. Although if I knew then what I was going to know by the end of the flight, I would have been more than happy to have treated said passengers to whatever fluids I could have spared without causing myself any permanent damage.

What, I ask, possesses some people to imagine that complete strangers are even in the slightest bit interested in their medical histories? I should have thought that the shortcomings of one's (you may choose from any of the following) digestive (including gall bladder), cardio-thoracic, pulmonary, renal, uterine (solely mentioned by those of a female persuasion) or articulatory systems should be kept exclusively for the ears of one's physician; and not for everybody within twenty feet. Certainly not when other people are trying to sleep or eat.

On top of which, as if determined to pile it all on a bit thicker, these people never think of getting their hearing checked while they were last with their medical consultant. I am quite sure they must be slightly below par in the acoustics department, or why else would they feel the need to raise their voices by at least forty or fifty decibels? I believe that one woman – from

Idaho, if the story told to me is true – was measured at seventy-three decibels above the normal volume needed for speaking whilst operating a pneumatic drill.

Unfortunately, it was between two such bellowers that I found myself on this particular flight. I have a feeling that the undersized fellow at the check-in might have had a hand in the matter, as I'm not sure what the odds must be against finding oneself located between two women of such a clamorous nature. Rather on the long side I should have thought. Although, thinking about it, there does seem to be a plethora of vocally-enhanced women around these days.

Could there be a genetic influence at work, I wonder? Or perhaps merely a working example of the adage that sense and volume do not always go hand in hand? Or was that - with the possible exception of Zuleika Dobson - beauty and a lust for learning? I know not. However, I am quite sure that no part of my collagen and calcium matrix is in the slightest bit masogenistically inclined. Ha! As if.

Anyway, there I was, seated between two women – I think that their names might well have been Persephone and Hecate (or if they weren't then they jolly well should have been) - whose sole purpose for the duration of the flight appeared to be the disintegration of both my cochleas, and all the other items associated with the act of hearing.

63

I tried to listen to my personal stereo, and stuffed the headphones so far into my ear that had they not been attached to narrow lengths of wire I fear that they might, even now, still be lodged somewhere within the confines of my mastoid antrum.

I ventured to ask the two women if they might like to sit next to one another: but they declined my invitation. Apparently both women suffered from hypermetropia, found that wearing their spectacles in a pressurised cabin gave them headaches, and thus they needed a gap of no less than three feet between them in order to see each other clearly while they spoke.

I was about to point out that 'speaking' hardly did justice to the volume they were employing, but thought better of it. To spend ten hours in such close proximity to a brace of Harpies would be justifiably classed as unfortunate. To then cause them displeasure would, I fear, have been tantamount to inviting Thanatos to pay me an earlier than expected visit. Fortunately, their colloquy was only destined to last (at full volume) for three and a half hours. In the lull that ensued when they partook of their luncheon it was, I have to say, a relief to be able to hear the noise of the aircraft's engines once again.

It was also a joy to be able to listen to my Puccini recordings. I cannot recall the age I was when I 'discovered' opera - I think it may well have been around my early thirties - but I am certain that the locale was the Grand Theatre in Swansea.

I had, on the day in question, been to Cardiff to watch England play Wales at the National Stadium. A lot of people used to call it the Arm's Park, but I had always been under the impression that that was the name of the ground used by the Cardiff rugby club and was, in fact, immediately alongside the international pitch. However, whatever the name, I watched the match; which, incidentally, was thoroughly enjoyed by all as the result was a 13-13 draw, thus allowing both lots of supporters to leave feeling satisfied with honours even.

Not that it would have really mattered for, as with all other rugby matches I have ever attended, there had been no trouble in the crowd: quite unlike attending a soccer game.

"And why is that?" I hear. "Are you suggesting a difference in the socio-economic make-up of the spectators?"

I don't think so. I think the reason is more likely due to a difference in the average level of intelligence: both of the players and those who go to watch. Admittedly, gone are the days when eminent orthopaedic surgeons were to be found amongst the rugby pitch protagonists (due in no small way to the fact that teaching hospitals used to choose good rugby players from the list of hopeful student applicants), but I still think that, on the whole, much nicer people are to be found with an interest in the game played with the ovoid rather than the spheroid ball.

Call me biased if you wish, but my understanding of soccer has always been that if a goal is scored, the goal-keeper shouts at the right-back, who shouts at the centre-half, who shouts at the inside-right, who then has to scream obscenities at the referee whilst simultaneously kicking him on his shins. Why has the term 'Eugenics' just popped into my head?

But back to Cardiff ... After the match, I attempted to find my way to the Cardiff Central railway station. I say attempted as there was an extraordinary number of spectators (mostly of a Welsh nature) milling around, and my progress was being intermittently hindered by somebody called Dai, or Delmie; or Daffyd. There may even have been a Denzil as well.

I would have cheerfully accepted the occasional impediment to my peregrination, but to have complete strangers throw their arms round me, spill some ghastly smelling beverage over my shoes — which, by the way, I had managed to keep clean until then by nimbly stepping round glistening pools of liquids that had once been contained within who knows what locales — and then invite me to come and meet their sister was stretching even my normally relaxed attitude to another culture's customs. One doesn't like to be rude, but what can you say about a nation which can assemble 60,000 of its inhabitants in one place and get them to sing about how much they love their saucepans?

Anyway, one of these aforementioned partisans touched me with his lugubrious demeanour (which, so he explained to me, was as the result of having mislaid the money that his dear mother had given him to pay for his train ticket back to Pontarddulais) so I stopped to see if I could offer any assistance.

The fellow was, by some extraordinary combination of Nature and Nurture, one of that rare breed – certainly in that part of the Principality - which feels distinctly uneasy about tapping another for some unearned sponduliks. I had to endure several minutes of a dirge concerning the above misfortune, during which he ventured to cajole me into parting with seven pounds Sterling in exchange for a ticket that, he assured me, would entitle me to an evening of unrestrained rapture. You will, I hope, understand that I have not quoted the gentleman verbatim, but simply trying to give you the gist of what he was attempting to say.

"Which evening?" I enquired, whilst trying to establish contact with a pair of glazed eyes; each of which was looking in different directions at the same time, and neither one of which was anywhere near where I happened to be standing.

"Thishevning," came the rather garbled reply.

"And where, pray tell?"

"Schw ... swish ... shooo ..." The man then put an index finger up to his mouth, while his right eye closed, and a very strange grin began to spread across his face.

I soon realised that quietly extricating myself from my predicament, without causing undue offence to the now steadily gathering crowd of onlookers, might take rather a long time and involve the use of social skills to which I had no access. I handed over a ten-pound note, and took a rather crumpled ticket from a rather crumpled hand in return.

"Woo ... woo-ooo ... swaney ... mun ... poocha-knee?"

I have to admit to not being fluent in the Welsh tongue: that is, I am unable to say any more than 'yakey-dah' or 'diolch yn fawr', and I was thus completely flummoxed by what the poor fellow was trying to say.

Then suddenly, as if noticing my perplexity, he announced, with a modicum of lucidity, that he would go and get his rail ticket from what sounded like a less than complimentary description of a fly-half and return with my change. I, with reciprocal clarity, told him that he was more than welcome to keep the change and, with a neatly executed backward step, a small wave and passable baritone rendition of the opening lines of Cwm Rhondda, I made my escape.

I waited until I had travelled a safe distance before turning to see if the recipient of my munificence had located his unfortunately-titled outside-half, when I observed him staggering towards a nearby hostelry. I then noticed the name of said establishment and the sound of plummeting pennies was plainly audible. All the same, I thought, a most peculiar place to purchase a railway ticket. However, I resisted the temptation to pass comment, continued on to the station and caught the first train that was heading in a westward direction.

After a few minutes I decided that I had better inspect whatever it was that I had purchased for the princely sum of ten pounds. A cursory examination of the contents of my hand enabled me to find a rectangular piece of soggy cardboard upon which I could just make out the word Swansea (that explained the swooshing noises that the gentleman was making), and I also spotted Gra.d, Th..tre, and L. ...eme. I reasoned that whatever it was, was taking place at the Grand Theatre in Swansea; but as to what it might be, I have to admit to being well and truly stumped. However, as the ticket further indicated that mystery was due to begin at 7.00 that evening and as it was only 5.15, I decided (a spur of the moment type decision you understand) - as the train would reach Swansea in twenty minutes - that I would toddle along to see what it was all about.

Well, you can imagine my surprise when I found out that I had bought myself a ticket to see Puccini's opera 'La Boheme'. Ah, the 'poocha-knee' bit. I also expect you can imagine the inner turmoil that I underwent as I struggled with my initial inclination to hightail it back to the station and my secondary desire not to throw away ten pounds.

The secondary desire won the battle. Not purely because of my parsimonious nature, which often prevents me from compounding money ill-spent by wasting it altogether, but because of the thought of having to fight my way back to the station against a swelling tide of well-oiled Welshmen brandishing giant vegetables.

So, with a rising degree of apprehension at the thought of spending two hours stuck in front of a stage full of cantors straining to reach high 'C's – when I had always thought that the high 'seas' was the best place for them – I found the seat that I had been allocated.

I should explain that my sense of foreboding was due to the fact I had been under the impression that opera was mainly to be enjoyed by those of a pretentious nature who had large bank balances that had been acquired either by accidents of birth or some kind of skulduggery. A place in which to be seen, rather than a venue in which to spend time enjoying arias pumped out by divas with large chests.

But my goodness me, was I in for some surprises. To begin with, certainly on that evening, the audience was composed mostly of very ordinary-looking people. Not a bulging wallet, or ego, in sight: and that has been the general composition every time I have been since. I cannot, of course, speak for the average assemblage that may grace the Royal Opera House in Covent Garden, but provincial theatres appear to be patronised by normal men and women: and long may that remain so.

Admittedly you will always find individuals who, when choosing their apparel for the evening, are obviously unsure of whether they were going to the Alhambra or the Allotment; or that the consumption of crisps and sweets wrapped in cellophane does not, in fact, add to the overall appreciation of the occasion. I do feel that theatres should have employees on duty whose sole function is to point out to these individuals the extent of their thoughtlessness. I am quite sure that a sharp tap across the forehead with a cricket bat would quickly bring the inconsideration to their attention.

The strangest thing though, is why so many of these particular patrons frequently seem to occupy the seats immediately behind mine. Whether I book over the telephone weeks in advance or purchase my ticket half an hour before the curtain is due to go up, there they are; with an impressive array of cacophonous confectionery at the ready. Such behaviour quite beggars belief. I am absolutely positive that when Puccini put quill to paper (I expect that dear old Giacomo would have used a fountain pen of some description, as the likes of Lewis Waterman and Walter Sheaffer were up and running around 1884 and La

Boheme was finished in 1896; but I think 'quill' sounds far more romantic) he did not envisage his compositions having to compete with certain avaricious sections of an audience who seem unable to go for more than thirty minutes without feeling the need to shovel comestibles down their throats.

As for the type of audience that awaits me when, on the rare occasion, I have the misfortune to visit a cinema .... Well, more of that later.

Anyway, there I was, in the Grand Theatre Swansea, all set to see a production of Puccini's La Boheme: and what an absolute joy of an evening I experienced. Serendipity unconfined. I had opened a package that I had chanced upon by the roadside; and instead of finding the remains of a stale mechanically-reconstituted meat sandwich, I had found an unopened jar of Beluga's finest.

I suppose I was rather fortunate that the ticket hadn't been for an opus by Wagner – not that there is anything amiss with any of Richard's pieces, but I have since found that they are a bit too heavy for my taste – or else a world of euphonious rapture would have passed me by.

Now, where was I? Oh yes, on the plane and about to withdraw into my world of 'tiny frozen hands' and 'one fine days'. Bliss. Or at least it should have been. Unfortunately that was when all the gallimaufry started.

For you see, when I listen to Puccini whilst travelling, I tend to lapse into a near coma-like state. For some reason best known to itself, my body shuts down and I float away, drawn high by the mellifluous tones to my own Nirvana. Friends who know me, realise that my stupor is only of a temporary nature and that a state of sensibility can be reintroduced by merely removing my earphones and gently whispering that there is a large gin and tonic to be found within easy reach.

Unfortunately, my on-board neighbours noticed my pallor and, after only a few seconds deliberation, decided that I was in the process of relinquishing my hold on this life, and alerted a

70

member of the cabin crew. So, instead of enjoying a gentle cerebral massage by Luciano Pavarotti and Rolando Panerai as they delivered their fine rendition of 'O Mimi, ti piu non torni', I found myself being dragged from my seat, laid flat on the floor and then subjected to a vigorous chest massage by an over-keen, and rather overweight, general practitioner from Hemel Hempstead.

I am still grateful to this day that I became cognisant of what was happening in time to prevent him from enveloping my oratory equipment within the not inconsiderable boundaries of what appeared – at least to a man coming out of a state of hibernation – to be the inner-tube of a mountain bicycle that had somehow managed to get attached to the area of his face that was below his equally considerable nose.

By this time, of course, quite a crowd had gathered; and as I struggled with the doctor from Hemel Hempstead, I could hear many voices offering all manner of advice in ways of assisting me back to the Earthly plane from which I hadn't actually departed in the first place. Some of the advice, although well intentioned I've no doubt, would probably have killed most people of a weaker constitution: and I'm sure that I only narrowly avoided an emergency tracheotomy and open-heart manipulation that was being suggested from one quarter, and the administration of a quite exotic range of suppositories from another.

What good the suppositories would have done, I've no idea, but I think they would have elicited a somewhat more vociferous response from me to the situation than "I say!" and "What on earth do you think you're doing?" You see, I have always regarded the orifice for which suppositories are intended as being specifically, and solely, designed for purposes of egress rather than ingress; and have no intention of changing that viewpoint.

It must have taken the best part of twenty minutes to convince everybody that not only was I not about to pop my clogs, but that I never had any intention of doing so in the first place. The suppository-advocating quarter, dressed in a rather garish shirt and cream pleat-fronted chinos, seemed decidedly disappointed (rather too obviously for my liking) that that was the case.

So, after several apologies had been proffered – none from me I hasten to add, as I felt that I was the aggrieved party in the preceding imbroglio – along with a half-bottle of Champagne by means of recompense, my journey was allowed to continue in the manner in which I had rather hoped for when I first boarded the aircraft.

I have to admit, with my usual degree of disarming modesty, that I accepted the apologies with an air of magnanimity that would have stood fair beside the one shown by Sam Houston towards Santa Anna at San Jacinto: and I managed to carry out my act of goodwill without recourse to the observation of any Masonic signs of distress. Indeed, not once did I spot, or receive influence from, a right hand placed on heart and an extended left hand.

In fact, had I spotted same, I might well have withdrawn my forgiveness. I have always had more than a touch of apprehension towards a grown man (free and of a mature age, to be exact) who feels the need to check for cowans and eavesdroppers before proceeding to roll up his left trouser-leg, don a blindfold, expose his left nipple, slip a cable-tow around his neck and then have someone press the tip of a compass to his chest. Call me cynical by all means, but it is, as I always say, more comfortable to sleep on a clear conscience than an expensive mattress.

But, to return to the subject of my largesse, I did display a slight discomfort about being offered Champagne as atonement for my ordeal. Not because I find the taste of Champagne unpleasant, quite the contrary in fact, but because of my previously mentioned aversion to anything French. Although, if truth be known, the British had more than a passing interest in the development of the sparkling stuff as they came up with a safe way of bottling it! Anyway, a short explanation resulted in the sparkling white wine from the Marne region around Reims and Epernay being returned to the fridge from whence it came, and an equally cold brace of large G'n'Ts taking its place.

The incident also resulted in my previously loquacious companions remaining taciturn until they scurried through customs at San Francisco International Airport; and that in itself was worth a bucketful of intoxicants.

Back to the flight. Before I allowed my attention to refocus on Puccini, I took time to inspect the electronic gadgetry attached to the arm of my seat.

I am the first to admit that great swathes of modern technology have completely passed me by. I know how to use my microwave oven, and I even know how to programme my video recorder. I can also, with reasonable confidence, claim to have mastered certain aspects of my mobile phone. Well, I really mean that I know how to make and receive calls: which, I suppose, is about as much as one should ask of one's telephone. I am afraid to say, however, that I have little or no idea how to perform most of the myriad of other functions of which the little fellow is capable.

Texting, I am sure, is relatively simple. One merely requires a working knowledge of the English language [*Stop Press* - I have just been informed that the content of most text messages bears little relationship to the English language with which I am familiar, and more to a cross between Shorthand and Dyslexo-Croat}, an acquaintance who owns equipment capable of receiving your message and - and this is probably the most important factor of all - fingers the size of matchsticks.

What, I ask myself, is the point of reducing the size of cellular phones until they have reached the dimensions of a wristwatch if the fingers that are to be found on the hands of most human beings are not also being similarly reduced in size?

I do not claim to be over-endowed in the digit department, either in size or number of said phalanges, but I will readily admit to having a great deal of difficulty in not pressing down two or three of the buttons at the same time. Now such a handicap would be fine if I knew someone whose telephone number was 25476980: but alas, I do not: nor ever have done. Perhaps I should try and cultivate friendships with such people. Is there a club that one could join?

Speaking of a surfeit of fingers ... Have you ever thought how different life would be if we had six digits on each hand instead of five? Did you realise that – apart from the obvious (namely having to redesign gloves) – arithmetic would be much simpler?

"Eh?" I hear you splutter. "How would it be simpler? How can you count to ten with twelve digits?"

"Aha," I reply. "You wouldn't have to."

"Uh?"

"You would employ the duo-decimal system of counting. Base of 12."

"And how, pray, is that easier. How does 12, 24, 36 and so on become easier than 10, 20 and 30?"

74

Now I have to admit that this is where I get a bit confused. But, apparently, by using 12 one is able do arithmetical problems a lot faster. It seems that where ten is only divisible by 2 and 5, twelve is divisible by 2, 3, 4 and 6. Does that explain things? No, it doesn't leap out at me either: but there we are.

Anyway, back to small telephones. Another problem with them is that I can never find the damn things. I think that when one purchases one of these miniature communication devices one ought to be supplied with another mobile phone – of sensible and manageable dimensions – which can then be used to ring the phone that you have misplaced. Rather in the same way that people often wish that they had a second pair of spectacles to help them find their first pair.

You will, I hope, have noticed that I have not mentioned anything about the third generation mobile phones – or '3G' as they like to be called – that are currently being inflicted upon us. What the heck is going on there? If I want a small video camera I shall go and buy one. If I want to watch videos on a one-inch screen I am quite capable of watching my current television from a distance of thirty feet or more. Why I should ever want to, though, is beyond my ken.

No, I feel that all this new technology is merely a result of wanting, yet again, to find new ways of making Joe Public part with his hard-earned cash. First you make him buy something he doesn't really need, get him used to it, and then, after a year or so, you announce that you have just made a much better version and that owning one would enhance his life considerably. This process can then be repeated at regular intervals.

But problems with size apart (no, I am not going down that avenue), these modern marvels of communication are capable of doing things that technophobes such as I have no chance of conquering. Not in this life anyway. And, speaking of 'phobes', why do they call it techno*phobia*? A 'phobia', to my knowledge, is an irrational fear; and I do not have an irrational fear of things technical: I simply fail to understand how to use them. Perhaps the term 'techno-thicko' or 'techno-no-no' might be more appropriate.

I quite willingly admit to having no idea how the blessed things work. In fact, anyone who has seen me struggle with one of these instruments will be left in little doubt that I am not operating it with the nonchalant air of someone tying up their shoelaces. Not for me the display of nimble fingers that seem to dance across the controls. Oh no. The degree of expertise shown is more like that of someone attempting to thread a needle whilst wearing oven gloves.

Having said that, however, I do not have my tongue sticking out of the side of my mouth whilst I struggle to press one key at a time; nor do I sweat as if I was trying to defuse an explosive device. A certain level of discomfort might, however, be exhibited: but let it never be said that I have an irrational fear of mobile telephones.

As I have, adequately I hope, pointed out, I have little or no idea how they work; but my lack of understanding is overshadowed by that belonging to my father.

"Oh, is your father short of a few dendrites?" I hear you ask.

"No," I reply. "Quite the opposite, in fact."

"Then is this inability to master objects with numbered buttons an inherited trait within the family?"

"Only in so much as dying is," I would further respond.

Let me elucidate for you. I can recall taking my father into a shop that sold mobile phones because I felt that one would be very handy for my parents as they enjoy driving. Well, my father enjoys driving: my mother, fortunately, is quite happy to be driven. Not that I wish to cast aspersions about her doubtful ability behind the wheel of a car: I don't feel that there is any need as there are plenty of others who would be more than capable of drawing your attention to that fact.

I simply thought it would be handy if they had a means of summoning help should their vehicle ever develop a mechanical problem. Younger, fitter, men would be more than capable – and probably quite keen if they had a passenger of the nagging female variety - of trekking several miles to beckon assistance; but I felt that my parents would appreciate a non-exertory means of accomplishing same. So a mobile phone it was.

But what sort? Obviously, as I have already mentioned, it would need to be one that could be managed by other than a combination of a micro-surgeon and a theoretical physicist: and mother wanted one that had a nice shape; and came in a nice colour.

Now I knew, or had a feeling at least, that choosing a suitable handset might prove to be rather laborious; but I was somewhat taken aback when, in response to a fairly reasonable enquiry by the salesman of whether he would like a WAP phone, my father replied, in an unnecessarily loud voice ... "I don't want anything made by bloody Italians."

Now, as I have already alluded to, my father is an amiable enough fellow, with an easy-going, sometimes pleasant, charm that would make one doubt that he had, indeed, carried out several meritorious actions during the Second World War. This, I have noticed, is a characteristic shown by many of his contemporaries. Not for them the surly belligerence shown by so many of the present-day inhabitants of these sceptred isles when asked to perform a task that might cut short their afternoon spent in front of the television: never mind being asked to do something that might cut short their life!

But this nonchalant joie de vivre of my father hides a near incapacitating tendency that seems to manifest itself whenever he is confronted with a task that involves electronic keypads. I have seen the man foam at the mouth when requested, usually by my mother, to record a particular television programme.

"Wouldn't you rather watch it while it's on?" he would ask. "I'm quite sure that the programme would be so much better if we watched it at the time of broadcast."

Occasionally even, "I have heard it said that watching recorded television programmes can cause all sorts of eye problems."

Strangely, though, the injurious possibilities would suddenly present minimal consequences if I happened to be in the house at the time and could facilitate my mother's request. But, and this always struck me as very peculiar, my mother would then develop an aversion to watching the recorded programmes. For some reason or another, she lets the video-tapes of recorded material gradually build up and up, until there are piles of the blessed things around the television.

"Why don't you watch them?" I would ask.

"When do I have the time?" would come the reply.

"When do you have the time!"

"Yes, when?"

You will have to excuse me if I don't give you the whole conversation – *ad verbatim* so to speak – as it has been known to continue for as much as half an hour without a hint of a satisfactory outcome. When does she have the time, indeed!

My mother and father spend about an hour every morning opening up the mountain of rubbish that falls through their letterbox: and when I say rubbish, I really do mean rubbish. Circulars from companies trying to purvey things that my parents would, in their younger days, have never given room in their thoughts; never mind in their house. Rabbit-shaped slippers for keeping your feet warm, plastic boxes for catching spiders, cloth strips for relieving the pressure of a tight-fitting brazier, and an extremely useful rear half of a ceramic dog that one is meant to position in one's flower bed to give passers-by the impression that a buried bone is being recovered. Personally, I just get the impression that a family pet and a petrol strimmer have recently come into contact.

These are items, I feel confident in saying, that most people would regard as absolute idiocy. Yet, my parents are to be found, sitting in their lounge, opening their letters, and wondering how on earth they ever manage to survive without a stress-free bra whilst living in a house full of spiders.

As the years have gone by, I feel more and more convinced that modern medicine has a lot of answering to do. Can you imagine how simple life would be if we all expected to hand in our notices at the age of sixty-five? From the viewpoint of the aging population there would be no expensive health insurance payments, no need to be fitted for incontinence pants or surgical stockings, no looking for your dentures in the cheese dip, and no having to sell your house in order to spend your concluding years dribbling away in a badly-run home for the senile and terminally flatulent.

And the advantages for the younger generation? Well, they wouldn't have to give up their seats (not that they very often do these days, I suppose – okay forget that reason), no having to save for their pension contributions, no putting up with elderly relatives over Christmas, fewer gloved/piped/trilbyed pensioners driving on the roads to hold them up, no long Wednesday queues at certain DIY stores full of people wanting to save 10% on an item that only costs a few pounds - and weighs even less - before they then ask if there is somebody available to carry it out to their car.

That reminds me of an incident that took place in a queue in one of those very stores. I can vividly recall it because it was one of those occasions when, and it doesn't happen very often, I had the good fortune to be standing behind someone whose brain functioned on the same wavelength as my own.

"Good fortune?" I hear some of you questioning. "Surely any brain function similarity to yours should come with a health warning."

I shall decline to parry such a remark (mainly because nothing witty has sprung to mind), and simply say that the episode involved a gentleman who wanted to purchase a tin of adhesive; and went thus ...

"Yes sir?" asked the rather vacant-looking girl on the till.

"I would like to buy some of this adhesive," replied the gentleman (in his early fifties I would have judged), "but there are only empty cardboard packets on the shelf." He then held one up to show the till-operator.

"Oh yeah," the girl said, before rubbing her nose with the back of her fingers. "That's because of solvent abuse, an' that. We aren't allowed to, like, sell none of it on them shelves because of in case yoofs come in to nick it."

"Yoofs?"

"Yeah. Like young people."

"Oh. And why would they do that?"

"So they can, like, sniff it."

"People do that?"

"Oh yeah."

"Out of the tins?"

"Oh yeah."

"Goodness."

It was at that point that I felt compelled to enter the conversation. "But," I began, "it's much better to get a plastic bag, put cotton-wool in it, and pour some of the solvent on top. You can then breathe in the vapours by holding the bag over your face. Much less mess."

"Really!" exclaimed the gentleman.

"Yes," I replied, noticing the look of horror on the young girl's face. "Works a treat." I then decided, on account of my latent acting ability I expect, to add a couple of facial twitches for good measure.

The young girl's complexion then went through all the shades of the visible spectrum, such was her irritation and consternation at my interruption: she then reached under the counter, unlocked a draw, and removed a small tin of the requested adhesive.

"Will there be anyfink else?" she asked the gentleman, looking sweetly in his direction whilst still managing to glare in mine.

"Yes please," he replied, "Could I have a plastic bag and some cotton-wool?"

At that point I thought the girl was going to die, such was the severity of the convulsions she suddenly appeared to suffer. I'm sure that schools should teach, or at least acknowledge, the art of irony before it gets lost completely.

Whilst I have mentioned irony – I do so dislike people who say 'ironic' when they mean coincidental, paradoxical, or bizarre. Also, just out of passing interest, I dislike it when people say pressurised instead of pressured. How on earth can you pressurise someone into doing something? Do you get them to first step inside a sealed chamber? And don't get me started on pled and pleaded.

So where was I? Oh yes, the mobile phone and my father's aversion to most things of a modern-day technical nature. This state of affairs has always surprised me as he is someone who can use a sextant, navigate by the stars, and he designed an original form of 'roll-on roll-off' wharf that was used on the River Thames: but there we are.

However, to go back a few – well, quite a few - steps, I was about to discover the joys awaiting me through the medium of the remote-control located in the side of the armrest of my seat on the plane.

The first point I should like to make is regarding the location of said device. I am a person favoured with a sensible size in the buttock arena, and, as I am not one of those unfortunate people who have (apparently through some familial predisposition – the 'greed-and-laziness' gene, I believe it's called) succumbed to scourge of obesity, I am able to inform you that my pelvic neighbourhood is generally contained within a perimeter of thirty-six inches. But even I experienced some difficulty in removing the appliance. Actually, I experienced quite a lot of difficulty: so much so that at one point I thought I was going to dislocate one of my hips.

81

I cannot imagine how much amusement might be educed if one was the proud owner of Iliac crests that could accurately describe themselves as being separated, as the crow flies, by a distance of twenty-four inches or more. I expect the first obstacle to present itself would be wedging one's ample dimensions within the confines of a seat that was really designed for someone half that size. Without, that is, having to liberally apply goose-fat in order to expedite the manoeuvre.

The second, presumably, would be finding a means of later extricating yourself without resorting to the use of a length of 4"x2" as a lever: and where can you find one of those when you really need it? Although, come to think of it, I did notice a couple of brackets near the toilet area that might well have been designed for holding planks of wood.

On top of which, if one had then to remove the remote-control from its receptacle, most of the flight would surely be spent getting in and out of the seat or contorting yourself into a variety of postures and annoying the heck out of your adjacent passengers.

The receptacle was, for some obscure reason, placed between the armrest and your right thigh; and that is not an easily accessible position if you happen to be the proud possessor of a right leg. I would have thought that somewhere on the back of the chair in front might have been a little more convenient: but nobody asked me.

As an addendum to the above, I did have the opportunity to spend several very happy minutes watching a rather large lady - from Germany, if I accurately judged the language she employed to express her discomfort – trying to squeeze her more than ample frame past a mere slip of a girl who was trying to negotiate her way with a trolley along the aisle.

I should mention at this point, that as well as having an instinctive dislike of the French, I am none too enamoured with those of German extraction either. Actually, I don't think I have any great liking for any Europeans. Having said that, I feel obliged to point out that I don't want to change or influence them in any way. The French are French, the Germans are German, and the Italians are Italian: and they'll just have to live with that.

By the same token, I want the British to remain British. I do not like the insidious way that certain people – quite a few of them unelected – seem hell-bent on destroying the very ethos of living in the British Isles. What was the name of the fellow who came up with the idea of a Federal Republic of Europe? Paul-Henri Spaak? Or was it Jean Monnet? One or the other: and they decided that the only way to achieve their goal – a politically integrated Europe – was to pretend that it was only a 'Common Market'.

Then that bloke d'Estaing went on to say that handing power over to Brussels would be 'hidden and disguised', and that people would be 'led to adopt the European Constitution without knowing it'. You'll have to remind me why it is that people have lost all faith in politicians.

As for the apparent uncontrolled immigration policy that seems to have been put in place ... Well, I just wish you could see the veins on my forehead throb whenever I think about multiculturalism. Ghastly concept. And should I mention NHS tourists and why it is that our taxes go towards treating people who have no right to be in the UK instead of caring for our own? No; I think, possibly, that is enough gloom.

Well, apart from getting one more thing off my thorax and asking why it is that a lot of people who 'flee' to these islands from countries where they were being 'persecuted', immediately set about trying to change the way we do things here? If people don't like our way of life, then don't damn well live here. How complicated is that? Oh, would that I could run things for a month or two.

But back to the amply proportioned German lady. Did I make a comparison with a certain Graf Spey? Or a certain drifting dirigible by the name of Hindenburg? No? Well, believe me, I most certainly could have.

I wasn't entirely sure what she was saying, but it seemed to contain words such as 'Lassen sie mich durch' and 'Sie wissen wer ich bin'. Now I am quite sure that nothing untoward was said – or intended – but whatever is being said in German always sounds to me as if plans are being drawn up to invade someone else's country. I will, albeit begrudgingly, admit that the French and Italian languages can have a friendly, even romantic, feel to them: but *German* ...

Anyway, it took quite a while before said Fraulein managed to squeeze past; treating, in the process, a rather diminutive fellow in an aisle seat to an earful of expletives and a generously proportioned Teutonic bosom. It was hard to tell if he was terrified or rather enjoying the experience. I, however, found it fascinating how the lady's body when pressed in one area seemed to billow out in another. It must be true when they say that gases can be compressed, but liquids cannot.

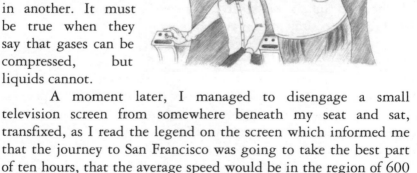

A moment later, I managed to disengage a small television screen from somewhere beneath my seat and sat, transfixed, as I read the legend on the screen which informed me that the journey to San Francisco was going to take the best part of ten hours, that the average speed would be in the region of 600 miles an hour, and the cruising altitude around 37,000 feet. I would even be able to watch the progress on a map that would appear if requested.

Next, with some rather interesting manoeuvres, I managed to remove the controls from the inside of the arm-rest (whilst also managing to press some of the buttons, which in turn switched on my overhead light, switched off my overhead light, and called one of the male members of the cabin-crew for assistance who, incidentally and for some reason that initially escaped me, brought to mind a row of tents), and decided to have a quick wander through the available channels.

Alas, my ability to carry out the procedure did not match my desire to do so. Try as I did to watch one of the many films available, I was unable to summon anything else apart from the map of where the plane was, a small furry animal that wanted to jump about collecting rings, an episode of 'On the Buses' and, once again, a male member of the cabin-crew. And all the while trying to keep my feet away from the queue of people waiting to avail themselves of the toilet facilities.

I decided to return to my Puccini.

Soon afterwards − or so it seemed − the plane began to make its descent to San Francisco airport. Ear-popping time once again. Makes one wonder how well sealed the fuselage really is! A few tilts, a quick view of the San Mateo Bridge, a couple of bumps, and there I was ... in the United States of America for the very first time.

Arrival in the USA

I don't know about you, but I always feel incredibly guilty when I walk towards customs officials. I try to appear jaunty ... but I invariably look furtive. I try to smile disarmingly ... I end up by sneering. I hold open doors for others ... I appear to loiter with intent. Must be something in the Phalarope genes, I suppose.

Anyway, I carefully approached an extremely large gentleman – who had no discernable neck, I might add.

"And what is the purpose of your visit?" he asked.

"I ... I'm not entirely sure," I replied.

"Huh?"

"I'm not entirely sure."

"Waddya mean, 'you're not entirely sure'?"

It was about this time that I began to wonder if the purpose of my trip had already started. I decided to maintain my composure and refrain from asking the gentleman if English was, indeed, his first language. I did, however, begin to speak very slowly – just in case. "I ... am ... not ... entirely ... sure."

"Huh?"

"What?"

"Listen buddy ..."

"I'm all ears."

"You're what!"

"Listening."

"So what is the purpose of your visit? Business or pleasure?"

"Well, as I have already indicated, I don't really know. I believe it's some kind of sociological research experiment."

"Huh?"

"Some kind of -"

"Never mind. Jeezus! How long are you here for?"

"Six weeks. I believe."

"You're here for a six week 'experiment'?"

"Got it in one."

"Yeah?"

"Absolutely."

"What kind of 'experiment'?"

"Again, not entirely sure. Something to do with a magazine."

86

"So will that be business or pleasure?"

"Who knows."

"Who ...! Where are you staying?"

"Sorry, can't help you with that either."

"Didn't you fill in a form on the plane?"

"What form?"

"The immigration form."

"Oh. Ah. Yes, I think I might have."

"Well where is it?"

"Here we are," I replied, after successfully searching my pockets.

"You've not put an address down."

"That's because I'm not sure where I'm going."

"Because ...! Sir, I'm gonna have to ask you step to one side while I call my supervisor."

I duly moved to the requested spot, much to the relief of those in the queue behind me, and awaited the arrival of the supervisor. A few quiet asides and a genial handshake later, I was allowed to go and collect my luggage. But not before a rather officious spaniel tried to gain access to my rucksack. Well, either that or the animal was trying to have sex with it: it's always hard to tell with some breeds.

Next, several more minutes were spent explaining that I had had a few grapes in my rucksack, that I had finished them all before I disembarked from the aircraft, and no I did not have any raw meat hidden about my person. Raw meat? What the dickens would I want with some raw meat 'hidden about my person'? Not exactly the sort of thing I would readily do in the privacy of my own home, I can assure you; never mind on an aircraft with a bunch of complete strangers. Very strange. Especially as people seem to fly into the UK without having to answer all those questions.

Mind you, after a short reflection, maybe such an undertaking might have avoided all that foot and mouth nonsense that we had to endure a few years back. But after further reflection, I doubt if any change in circumstances would have made one iota of difference – given the blithering idiots, under secret orders from Brussels so I believe, that we had running the show at the time. There are times, you know, when I really do despair at the lack of backbone showed by some of my compatriots. We really do put up with an awful lot of people – who have no damn right – telling us what to do.

What was that W. H. Auden poem? Oh yes,

To save your world, you asked this man to die.
And would that man, if he could see you now,
Ask 'Why'?

Makes me want to weep, it really does: both the sentiments of the words and the state of affairs that prevail in Great Britain. Very sad.

Anyway, after having retrieved my large case from the carousel, I made my way to the arrivals area.

I had spent several minutes standing out like a bit of a sore thumb when I was approached by an Oriental-looking chappie and, probably a tad rudely as I was unsure if he was trying to sell me something, I did my best to ignore him.

"Are you Mr Farropee?" he finally managed to ask, after we had danced around a little.

"No," I replied.

"Wir-rem Farropee?"

"No."

"Are you Igreesh?"

"Igreesh! No I jolly well am not."

"No? You sound Igreesh."

"Well sir, I can assure you that I am not. I happen to be English; but I fail to see what business that can be yours. Now go away."

"Are you sure you not Wir-rem Farropee?"

"Yes. Quite sure."

"You from Eeen-grand?"

"I am from England, and my name is William Phalarope"

"That's whah I said."

"No it wasn't. You said Farropee. Not Phalarope."

"Whah-evah ... it crose enough. You follow."

"But I - "

"Please."

I followed.

John Wayne Kitabayashi (as my companion soon introduced himself) drove to the City (as the residents prefer to call San Francisco – apparently they really dislike the term 'Frisco') along a thoroughfare known as Highway 101; followed by, if my understanding of J.W. Kitabayashi was correct, something to do with licking someone's Ness. It all sounded a bit unsavoury to me; but being a polite sort of fellow, I kept quiet.

About half an hour after leaving the airport, we arrived at our destination - Taylor Street – not too far from an imposing religious building known as Grace Cathedral, and in an area that was known as Nob Hill.

"Velly plestigious," he added.

I thanked Mr Kitabayashi for his guidance, slipped him a suitably-sized note, exchanged three or four shallow bows, and then waved him a cheery adieu. It was then that I realised I had no idea where I was or who I was supposed to meet.

My discomfort was, fortunately, short-lived as standing outside the building was a Greek-looking gentleman who introduced himself as Joel. I should, perhaps, say that by 'Greek-looking' I mean swarthy; rather than covered in Taramasalata and bits of broken crockery.

Joel, it transpired, was the owner of the flat (or apartment as they prefer to be called over there) that was to be my home for the next few weeks; and he wanted to show me round in person. The reason for staying in the apartment, apart from the fact that it was going to be a lot cheaper than an hotel, was that it would allow me to get closer to the 'feel' of the City.

Fair enough, I thought; and Joel was happy as he was going to be out of town for the duration of my stay, and this arrangement meant that his apartment wouldn't be left empty for that time.

The tour of said apartment didn't take all that long as the apartment wasn't all that long: or wide. Joel described it as being a one-bedroom studio apartment. Hmm, I remember thinking. I'll go along with 'studio': I'll even go along with 'apartment'. The 'bedroom' bit did confuse me somewhat though. He had got the 'bed' bit right, but I was left a little befuddled about the 'room' part. 'Area' might have been more accurate.

I have to admit to having had no real idea about apartment sizes in San Francisco; but I had imagined that they would be mostly big and plush, and well equipped. Well, the one belonging to Joel wasn't: and, if what I generally heard was correct, quite a few others were also on the small side of average. The price of property in the City, however, was not; and that was why so many people rented their accommodation. Mind you, I think I would be a little hesitant to lash out oodles of readies to buy a house that was built on one of the major fault lines of the planet. But that's just me.

Now I know that people witter on about the importance of location, but I am certain which one my finger would point to if (and here I must make a comparison between locations back in the UK) I was offered a choice - from a comparative price point of view - between a shoe-box in South Ken and a four-bedroom detached property with sea views in South Wales. A postcode with SW7 on it might impress some people, but I, I'm quite happy to say, do not appear amongst that number.

No indeed. Give me some good views, quiet neighbours, decent off-road parking, no chance of being mugged on the way home, and I'm a happy soul. Not for me the rush-hour crush, blaring radiograms and thirty minutes spent looking for a parking spot within half a mile of my front door.

Anyway, the apartment. It was, as I have mentioned, in a very nice part of San Francisco. It had a front door, a short corridor, a bathroom, a kitchen, and a lounge. The bedroom, as I started mentioning, if it could be called a 'bedroom' (although I have met several estate agents who would have no qualms about doing so) was inside an 'area' that was just big enough to contain the bed. The bed was about six and a half feet by five, and the 'area' – which only had two walls and a pillar where the third and fourth walls would have met – was also about six and a half feet by five.

Joel, as I was to discover, was a bit of an artist, and had hung quite a few paintings on the walls of the apartment. I am not going to comment on the standard of said works of art as I am in no position to pass critical judgement on same; but I would have preferred it if every single light in the place hadn't been directed upon them. I like a light to shine in such a way that I, without fear of injury, can find my way around; or be able to read without standing and holding my scroll up against the wall. Joel, it appeared, did not. Nor did he seem particularly interested in looking at what he was cooking, shaving or washing up either.

As for the electrical sockets, trailing leads and the insulatory capabilities of most of his electrical appliances ... well, the less said the better. I know that the USA only has about 110 volts (as opposed to our 230), but I am quite sure that 110 volts up the old kazooma on a regular basis would not be appreciated. I imagine that even once or twice would be very irritating.

Whilst I'm on the subject of unexpected bursts of electricity, during one of my many visits to a library (about which I shall elaborate later), I did a little bit of delving into the various means of Capital Punishment. Heavens, do they have some fun over in the USA.

I have a vague recollection of the last two people – Peter Allen and John Walby – to be hanged in the UK, (August 1964) but, at the time, had no understanding of the arguments for and against the procedure. Needless to say, my understanding, and ability to argue comprehensively, about the subject has developed considerably over the ensuing years.

But that is not the issue here. What puzzles me is the fact that I can be sitting in my bath, inadvertently allow the electric radio to slip into the water and – at 230 volts – find myself trundling off to meet my maker in no time at all. But allow the American Criminal Justice system to strap me to a chair, attach electrodes to my head and to my calf muscles, wire me up to 2000 volts, and I might take quite a while before I finally shuffle off my mortal coil. As for what dreams may come – well, they would certainly give me plenty of pauses.

I know that the electric chair was the brainchild of a dentist (Alfred P. Southwick of Buffalo) – which might account for the pain side of things – and that there was a bit of a kafuffle between Thomas Edison and George Westinghouse about whether the DC or AC current worked best: but all the same.

Then we have the Lethal Injection, Lethal Gas and that old favourite, the Firing Squad. Happy days! No, after all is said and done, hanging has to be the preferred choice. Albert Pierrepoint reckoned it usually took about 26 seconds from the time he came to get the condemned man to the time death occurred; so I think that method would get my vote: unless I could take some tablets and a couple of whiskies. What's that other stuff? Oh yes, Sodium Pentobarbital. A quick swig of that, a few Zs, and then off you pop. Highly civilised. Although, now I think about it, I did hear that breathing increasing levels of Carbon Dioxide is a far from unpleasant way to hand in your notice. Or, whilst the grey matter is on a bit of a roll, is the 'cruel and unusual' aspect the whole point? Another discussion for the dinner table!

How on earth did I manage to wander down that road? I wasn't making fun of America's ability to complicate matters was I? As if I would. Anyway, back to the apartment and its woeful lighting arrangements. Oh, I've done those. What next? Actually, I shouldn't really be making any complaints … it wasn't as though it was costing me anything. Maybe I should mention the instructions that Joel left for me.

First of all, I was not to answer the door.

"Why not?" I asked, not really thinking I would anyway, as the front door was two floors down.

"Because it's nearly always a solicitor."

Odd, I thought; "Oh," I said.

"Yeah. And they are a real nuisance."

"My sentiments exactly." Maybe this chap Joel wasn't such a flake after all. I could prate for hours about the encounters that I have had with solicitors, about the amount of money that they have cost me, about the dreadful barristers that they have recommended, about ... Well, about all manner of things that have made my life, and many others I'm sure, quite a lot worse than it was before they entered it. But, as I intimated, life is short enough as it is.

"So don't let any in."

"Absolutely not."

"Don't let them sell you anything."

"You have my word on that."

"But you may get a visit from the person in the flat above."

"Oh."

"Yeah. Nartor. Nartor's okay though."

What Joel had omitted to tell me about Nartor was – Well, let me describe the time he called.

There was a knock on the apartment door one evening, so I traipsed over to answer it. I think it was probably just as well that I was feeling a bit on the sleepy side, else, upon opening the door, I might have jumped backwards whilst emitting a noise not dissimilar to air escaping from a car tyre.

"Oh ... hello," I finally managed, after recovering as much of my symmetry as I could muster.

"Hel-looowww," came the soft reply. "My name is Nartorrrrrr. I'm from the flat above you."

"Hello, again. I'm William." I gingerly accepted the extended arm and carefully shook the hand that was on the end of it. I think it might be helpful of me to explain the reason for my slight state of disorientation.

The person in front of me seemed – and I must emphasise that I was a trifle on the heavy-eyed side of alert, but not, repeat, not intoxicated – to be a lady of about fifty years old, and about seven months pregnant. Reason enough for amazement: at least for me. But, just in case it wasn't, Nartor (of the rolling Rs) had opted for the blow to the solar plexus approach; and was wearing something like a kaftan, had very slim wrists, soft hands, a fragile build, and was sporting an aggressively bushy moustache.

"How nice to meet you ... William. You'rrrrre English, arrrren't you?"

"Er ... yes ..." I had often wondered what it might be like talking to Eartha Kitt: I was now, albeit vicariously, getting the opportunity to find out.

"Is Joel not back yet?"

"Er, no; no he isn't."

"Are you settling in?"

"Oh yes, thank you."

"Gooood."

The conversation actually went on for several more minutes: I can't be exactly sure how long, as I spent most of it trying to decide if Nartor had originally been a male or a female, had got partway through some form of 'gender reassignment' undertaking, but hadn't been able to make the final payment.

My question was never answered as, with a wave and wishes of "You have a good one", Nartor wended his – or her - merry way back up the stairs.

As well as a number of other matters about which I have little experience, I feel I ought to mention the one involved with errata concerning physical and emotional sexuality: and matching up of same. I have had occasion to read several articles about people who regard themselves as having been billeted in the wrong body. You know the sort of thing – man in woman's body and vice versa. Actually, I think that I may have touched earlier on the subject. But anyway, all terribly disconcerting.

Mind you, I can think of other examples – videlicet, people who reckon (as in the case of that Lilliputian at the check-in desk) that the body they were meant to have was at least a foot longer, or narrower, or better looking than the one they were given. I suppose that one ought, from time to time, to stop and count the blessings that were handed out in one's own direction. Gratia Dei and so forth. Life is a funny old business, isn't it? And it takes a jolt to make you aware of its passage. Rather like only being aware of your brain when you have a headache.

Which puts me in mind of another of Life's paradoxes – if time flies when you're having fun, should you do boring/tedious things to make it seem longer? If you lead an exciting life, does it end up feeling like a short one? Another case of exam first, lesson afterwards, I suppose. But enough profundity.

And then a jolly odd thing happened. For the first occasion in my life, I found time to consider such as Nartor as being unfortunate (in my eyes, that is) - rather than peculiar – and, much to my surprise, felt a tinge of compassion as well. You will have noticed that I didn't say I felt 'sorry' for Nartor – as I have no doubt that he felt blessed in many ways – just that I had been made aware of the way that different people are dealt different cards in Life and it's how you play your hand that matters. This time I really do mean enough profundity.

A Street Fair.

So there I was, on a fine Sunday afternoon – the last
Sunday in September as it happens – casually strolling along a
thoroughfare that went by the name of Seventh Street: which,
incidentally, finds itself between Sixth and Eighth street. Hardly
imaginative, one has to say, especially as they start at First and go
all the way up to around Twentieth.

If you think that lacks creativity, then you ought to take a
quick squiz at the range of names used for the avenues. Second
through to Forty-eighth! Except – as with the streets – there is no
Thirteenth; and instead there is one called Funston Avenue.
Maybe there was a shortage of creative street-namers at the time.
Come to think of it, I believe that an Irishman may have been
involved with the layout of the place.

Another part of the City has streets that have been named
in alphabetical order. Anza Street is next to Bilboa Street, which
is next to Cabrillo. 'D' and 'E' seem to have skipped town, and
then comes Fulton. The Golden Gate Park looks as though it has
swallowed 'G' and 'H', before we resume with Irving, Judah,
Kirkham, Lawton, and so on until Wawona and Yorba. No 'Z'
however: and Lincoln Way comes before Irving. But, apart from
those minor inconsistencies, finding out where a particular street
is in relation to the others, purely depends on having a working
knowledge of the alphabet. And, as there are no sneaky curves and
the blocks are a fairly constant gap apart, you can always be quite
cognisant of where you are.

Anyway, back to my whereabouts. I was wondering along
Seventh Street – for no other reason than I just happened to be in
the area – when I noticed some rather oddly attired people
heading in a Southerly direction. My natural curiosity, or perhaps
I was merely being downright nosey, gave me a nudge and I
nonchalantly followed.

A turn to the right and then to the left - or perhaps it was the other way round (you will shortly understand the reason for my forgetfulness) - when I happened upon a small cordon at which a gentleman (at least I think it was a member of the male section of the human species – it was rather hard to tell as he/she was wearing a see-through sequined ball gown and a platinum-blond wig that was large enough to give shelter from an overhead sun to a small crowd that may have had occasion to gather in the vicinity) was, with a couple of similarly clothed individuals, asking for the princely sum of three dollars for access to whatever it was that lay beyond.

Not being one to fork out any legal tender for something that, at best, would be described as 'sight unseen', I decided to carry out an Italian Army attack manoeuvre. However, before I was able to place either of my feet in a backward direction, I was summarily swept forwards within the middle of a throng of people who were both eager to gain admittance and disinclined to pay for the privilege.

"Well," I hear you begin to articulate. "What did you find within?"

"Well," I begin to reply, "I'm not sure I can adequately describe what bombarded my poor organs of sight."

For the cognoscenti amongst the readers, I had stumbled into the middle of one of the best-attended Folsom Street Fairs for many a year.

"Oh!" I can hear the better-informed uttering. Maybe even an "Ah!" or two. Quite! How can I best illustrate what images proceeded to land upon my macula luteas?

To begin with, I noticed a gentleman who – wearing only a very small, very tight pair of leather shorts – was furiously, and in a most unhealthily provocative fashion, dancing away with only himself for company.

"So what?" I hear the question being swiftly raised. "Perhaps he danced like one of those inebriated uncles you often find at weddings, and it was simply that nobody wanted to accompany him."

The 'so what' of the matter was that said gentleman was doing his dancing inside a small cage.

"Well?" you continue. "People often are to be seen dancing away inside cages. Perhaps not at a wedding; but they are very popular in certain establishments, don't you know."

Of that I have no doubt - not from personal experience, you understand, just hearsay. However, the cage in question was being dangled on the end of a crane, about seventy feet above the crowd below.

"Your point being ...?"

Perhaps because of the rather moderated cloisters within which I normally subsist, I have been excused such sights on an everyday - or even an occasional - basis. Perhaps because I spend most of my time looking down at my feet when I perambulate I have been unfortunate enough to miss what might amount to hundreds of such overhead dangling phenomena.

Just as well, then, that I have no desire to help elect a pope; or else the chanting of 'Testiculos habet et bene pendente' wouldn't mean very much to me. Once again, my innate propriety forces me to decline from elaborating!

But I am quite certain that I would have noticed a crowd that was dressed in the fashion of those whom I presently found around me.

I think a small proclamation such as "Well I never!" or perhaps "Good heavens!" may have passed my lips. Perhaps even both. But neither would have come close to doing justice to what I saw parading - in a highly congested manner I might add, in case you wish to sympathise with my increasing air of discomfort – all around me.

A little technique that might assist you in coming close to appreciating what assailed my sensibilities entails lying down, preferably in a dark and quiet location, and letting your mind empty itself of all superfluous stimuli. Now let your (hopefully) fertile and (even more hopefully) robust imagination conjure up a street that is filled with people who have taken it upon themselves to congregate wearing the most extraordinary selection of leather straps, and chains, and – in a large number of cases - nothing else!

How is your imagination doing so far? Struggling? Well, just to lay it on a bit thicker, I now want you to create the image of some rather hirsute individuals who, for whatever reason, have decided to wear 'chaps' – you know, those leather things that cowboys used to wear over their ordinary trousers when they had to spend all day in the saddle.

"Some of those cowboys looked rather fetching in their 'chaps'," I hear you mutter.

I am quite sure they did. But I somehow doubt if those cowboys wore nothing underneath (especially if they intended to spend many hours sitting on a hard leather saddle) or, in the case of one particular gentleman - who was rather over-endowed in the buttock department - a pair of pink, and very sheer, lady's panties.

Now believe you me, these gentlemen looked unsavoury enough from behind, but that hardly came close to the jolt I received when I had the misfortune to see them from the obverse viewpoint. I can only express my gratitude that I wasn't inclined to ask them for directions, as I dread to think what they might have used to indicate upon which bearing I needed to proceed.

Furthermore, if all that wasn't bad enough, I was also treated to the sight of people wearing dog collars (and I mean *real* dog collars, rather than those of a priestly nature) who were being led along by a companion with the use of a lead. And, on many occasions, the person wearing the dog collar was also wearing high-heels, a feather boa, and, once again, very little else.

Then there was the rather unnerving spectacle of a man who had been strapped, in an upright position, onto one of those trolley things that people use to move heavy boxes; and, rather in the fashion of Hannibal Lector (complete with leather face mask, I might add) was being wheeled around.

But, probably, the highlight – from an intellectual point of view, of course - for me was stumbling across an area that seemed to have attracted quite a sizeable crowd of onlookers.

Yes, I know that most normal people would have high-tailed it out of there by now, but my initial sense of shock had, by this time, been numbed somewhat by the plethora of images raining down upon it: so I worked my way to the front. Or as near the front as I needed to before my height allowed to me see what had caused the fascination: and there was I thinking that I had seen it all.

What now hoved into view was the 'Society of Janus Charity Spanking Booth'. I jest not. Perhaps I should say it again. The Society of Janus Charity Spanking Booth. Doesn't really seem any better the second time around, does it? Or make any sense either. Perhaps I ought to take a moment to describe what I saw there.

In the midst, appearing for all the world as if it was entirely normal and with about as much awkwardness as if it had been taking place in the privacy of her own home, was a woman, lying down on a table of some description, wearing just a Basque and stockings, who was being spanked by another woman.

I can sense the pupils of most men dilating as they read that. However, I feel obliged to add that the woman being spanked was an extremely large woman; and that the portions of flesh on display were unpleasantly dimpled, and wobbling about in a manner that struck an extraordinary balance between a jelly and a Mexican wave.

Perhaps I should also add that the woman administering the rather bizarre form of Corporal Punishment was wearing a pair of weight-lifting gloves and an expression that gave me the feeling she had performed the procedure on countless previous occasions. Perhaps, even, she would rather have been attending the funeral of a close, and much loved, member of her immediate family. She may well have preferred to be performing the act on the recently deceased as well. We shall never know.

I then happened to notice a rather seedy-looking fellow alongside, who had been stripped to his underwear, tied to some kind of wooden A-frame, and was in the process of being whipped by an over-enthusiastic member of the crowd. But I would, if you don't mind, prefer not to dwell on that image for too long as I am shortly going out for dinner.

So who was Janus, and why should his society be interested in spanking people? The first question can be easily answered: Janus was the Roman god of gates and doors, beginnings and endings, represented with a double-faced head with each looking in opposite directions. I have to admit, that if I were a god I think I would prefer to be in charge of something like war, or the sea, or fire; or even barren wives. But to be in charge of gates and doors? Hardly stirs the blood, does it?

I think I would also have preferred a slightly better name. Something along the lines of Zeus or Poseidon, Apollo or Vulcan. But Janus? I can well imagine that he got teased rather a lot at school. I can just hear the other 'godlings' shouting "Here comes Janus the Anus," - or something equally disconcerting.

However, there was an aspect to Janus that might explain the society that adopted his name. He represented, amongst other things, the transition between primitive life and civilisation. I shall leave you to draw your own conclusions.

By now, I was beginning to realise that the Folsom Street Fair is an annual excuse for certain members of society to parade themselves in an extraordinary assortment of S&M paraphernalia. I was originally going to say 'American' society, but, if the range of accents being volleyed about was any indication, I would have to say that quite a few of the participants had travelled many miles to attend the bizarre fest.

Another strange aspect that I observed about those present was that – unlike the impression resulting from my hitherto understanding – rather a lot of the men must have, to put it mildly, drunk long and deeply from cups overflowing with testosterone. Men that would have made Desperate Dan look about as butch as your sister. Bearing in mind, of course, that I have never met your sister; who may, in fact, possess qualities that enable her to pull a bus with her teeth, and require her to shave on an hourly basis in order not to frighten small children as they travel home from school.

But those irregularities aside, I am talking about men who were covered in so much hair that their open shirts looked like burst sofas. Men who were bristling with so many muscles that a deputation of cannibals would have enjoyed lean meat for weeks. Men who – well, let's just say that I was extremely glad that none of them took a shine to me, for I very much doubt that I would have been strong enough to put up sufficient resistance!

Rather strange the sort of anomalies that Nature chucks up from time to time, don't you think? Meet one of those fellows down at your local, and visions of the SAS and other special forces would parade through your imagination. I rather doubt if pictures of leather wrist-straps and negligees are even in the queue.

But - and this was where the pitiable (maybe compassion was poking its head above the parapet once more) side to the whole proceedings came into play – there was also a large number

102

of pathetic old men there. Men to whom Nature had not been kind: or generous. Men who were of an age where time should have provided them with enough sense, and dignity, to keep their inclinations – and some unimpressive parts of their anatomy - well under wraps. And I don't mean wraps of a leather nature! Or, as was currently the fashion, 'Pleather': which, for the uninitiated, is a mixture of plastic and leather. An absolute must, apparently, for those hot, humid days that are often to be found in San Francisco.

I am not going to begin a debate about the rights and wrongs of feeling the need to parade oneself in a manner that, at the very least, can be described as unusual; but I dread to think of the psychological damage that might result from spotting a previously clandestine follower of leather fashion items – say, one's father (or mother) - amongst the participants. Mind you, seeing your bank manager might prove advantageous should you ever feel the need for a loan!

All in all, a bit of an eye-opener, and no mistake.

I get a phone call.

I forget exactly what time it was, but I do recall my afternoon siesta being disturbed by what sounded like a small pelican trying to clear its throat. Now what a small pelican (whether white or brown, or with any affiliation to Louisiana) might have been doing in the apartment I had no idea: but I was in San Francisco, so it could have been visiting the island that bears its name. Whatever the reason for its presence, I proceeded to crawl about on the floor in an effort to locate the source of the, by now, rather infuriating sound.

"Eh?" I said, when I found what I now know to be a telephone, but at the time I perceived to be a rather large frog sitting inside a walnut cabinet. I pulled said amphibian out; having first, with the aid of my walking stick, established that the alarmingly realistic facsimile was just that.

Then, when I realised what the object was, I said, "Hello." After, that is, a couple of attempts, while I worked out into which end of the green monster I was meant to speak.

"Joel?" came a slightly weak reply, made all the more bizarre as it emanated from the animal's nether regions.

"No," was my response.

"No?"

"No."

"Well who are you?"

"My name is William."

"Oh really."

"Yes."

"William."

"Yes."

"Do I know you?"

"I have no idea. I can't say that your voice is pulling hard in any campanology sense."

"Campa what? Are you making some kinda insinuation here?"

"Some kind of *insinuation*? What are you talking about?"

"Are you saying there's something wrong with the way I speak? Are you? Hmm?"

"With the way you speak? What - " It was then that some of the fog which had mysteriously appeared began parting. I am usually the first to admit that the mill of my cognitive processes has a tendency to grind a bit slowly on occasions; but it does grind quite finely: on occasions. "My dear chap, campanology is the art of bell ringing. I meant that your voice wasn't ringing any bells with me."

"Oh. Right."

"Good. So ... why do you want to know if I know you?"

"Why! What do you mean *why*? Do you know who I am? Do you? Hmm?"

"Well, obviously not."

"Do you want me to tell you? Hmm?"

"If you wish for this conversation to proceed along normal channels, I think that would be a sensible idea. I'm not very good at this twenty questions lark."

"Well, I'm Ron. And Joel and I are in a committed and, I'll have you know, an exclusive relationship. We are an item."

"Ah ..." Strange how one's thoughts always seem to dissolve rather when a chap mentions something like that. But I took a deep breath all the same. "I am so glad. Really I am. Yes, indeed."

"So if you have any ideas about taking him away from me, I'll also have you know that I can turn nasty. And I mean *real* nasty."

"I'm quite sure you can. But I rather think -"

"So who are you? Hmm? And what are you doing in my Joely's apartment?"

"I was just about to -"

"Well?"

"If you would just rest your larynx for a moment I'll tell you."

The line then went very quiet. Next I thought I heard the sound of sobbing.

"Hello," I said, feeling like a bit of a beast.

The sobbing continued.

"Hello ... Ron?" I asked.

"Oh my god, you remembered."

"I did! Remembered what?"

"My name. So few people are prepared to make that kind of effort these days. Thank you so much."

"Er ... yes. Marvellous." I have to admit that I was more than little confused at that stage. "Right ... Ron," I blustered. "Um ... what can I do for you?"

"Are you ... British?"

"Yes."

"I thought so. I just adore the British accent."

"Thank you; it's one of my favourites."

"And you are so polite."

"Thank you once again."

"Are you a ... 'friend' of Joel's?"

"Ahm ... "

Now bearing in mind I wasn't really meant to be staying at Joel's apartment - as the magazine had sublet the apartment from Joel, and the contract that Joel had with the owner of the building meant that he wasn't supposed to sublet at any time - I knew that my feet and my mouth had to be kept well apart. Very complicated, but the bottom line was that I had been told to tell anyone who asked that I was a friend who was 'house-sitting' while Joel was away.

" ... Yes," I continued.

"Oh. Joel never mentioned you."

"He didn't? No, I, er, suppose he might not have."

"So what kind of 'friend' are you then? A 'close' one?"

"Oh no. No, no, no. Good heavens, no. That is, not, er, as such ... no."

"No? Oh good. Oh, I'm so relieved."

So was I, I don't mind admitting.

"So where is Joel?" Ron continued. "Is he there?"

"Not at the moment, no. I believe he's somewhere in Europe."

"Europe! Europe? When did he leave?"

"A few days ago."

"Well! He never said a word. Oh what a bitch! Just wait 'til he gets back. I'll have such - Did he say when he was returning?"

"Not specifically. But I would imagine that it won't be for a few more weeks."

"Damn him. How inconsiderate can one man be? Did he leave a forwarding address?"

"Not with me, no."

"Jeez … what am I …? Oh my, I've just remembered, I've got tickets for … We were meant to be going to … Hey William, do you like opera?"

"Opera? Well, er … I have, er, been known to … yes."

"Puccini?"

"Ye…es."

"Now listen William, I just happen to have two tickets to see 'Turandot' tonight. Do you pronounce it Turan-dot or Turan-doh?"

"I believe that either will do. Personally I say the dot as dot. I believe the word is Turandokhtar – meaning the daughter of a Turan. Dokhtar shortened to Dokht. Puccini, however, always pronounced it Turan-doh. Apparently that way it fitted the music better."

"Makes sense, I guess. Anyhoo, would you like to come along to it with me?"

"Well … I …"

"Oh go on, it'll be sooo much fun."

"Well … that is … I think …"

"You'll be my guest. And any friend of Joel's is a friend of mine."

"But I thought you said … that …"

"Oh *please*."

"Um … yes … Thank you. That would be … very nice. Yes."

"You will! Oh, that's just wonderful. Would you like me to pick you up?"

"No!" Thinking back, that might have sounded a bit sharp. "That is… I… what I mean is… Where is it being held?"

"In a really nice thee-ay-ter on Van Ness. Do you know it?"

"Which? Van Ness or the theatre?"

107

"Van Ness."

"I have a map."

"Oh, you British are so organised. What part of Britain are you from?"

"At the moment I'm living in Wales."

"Wales? Is that near Eye-er-land?"

"No."

"But that's Britain ... right?"

"What is?"

"Eye-er-land."

"Actually, no. Ireland isn't part of Britain."

"No! Gee ... I never knew that. So what part of Britain is Wales?"

"Can you picture the British Isles?"

"Kinda. I guess."

"Well, Wales is on the left side as you look at it. Shaped a bit like a pig's head."

"Oh ... Oh dear, I don't have that picture."

"Maybe it would be better if I draw you a diagram later."

"Ooh, yes, I'd like that."

"Yes. Quite. Okay then ... Well, um, what time and where?"

"Excuse me?"

"Where and when shall we meet?"

"Oh ... right. Well, I'm gonna need a little while to get ready. Got to look my best for my new friend, doan I?"

"You do? Really, there's no need to go to any trouble."

"William ... I insist. I don't want you thinking that I'm just some kind of flippertigibbet."

"I really wasn't going to think that." *Actually, that wasn't quite true!*

"Believe you me, William, there are some people who would. Now, let me think. What am I gonna wear so you know how to recognise me? Umm. We don't want the red carnation, do we? That is so passé. What do you think William?"

"I really ... wouldn't ... "

"I know; I'll wear my new jacket. You'll just love it. It's so me. Yes, that's what I'll do. I'll be wearing my new jacket. Do you know much about materials?"

"I wouldn't have thought so."

"No? I'm surprised."

"You are?"

"I most certainly am. You have such an artistic cadence to your voice."

"I do? Goodness me!"

"Oh yes. I can spot these things, you know."

"You can?"

"Oh yes. I studied thee-ay-ter. I'm very thee-atrical."

"Yes, I had rather, er, thought that."

"You did! Oh that is so nice of you. Okay then ... let me think. I'll stick to colours. It's a beautiful powder blue. Absolutely adorable. Will you be able to spot that?"

"I have a feeling I'll manage to."

"Good. And what about you? How will I know you?"

I have to hold up my hand and admit I felt like saying that I'll be the one hiding behind an enormous newspaper whilst running in the opposite direction: but I resisted. "I'll be wearing a dark sports jacket, white shirt and blue tie."

"Is that all?"

I then heard some extraordinary girl-like laughter. "Ah ... no," I managed.

"Pity. What colour pants will you be wearing?"

"I say! That's a bit personal, isn't it?"

"Excuse me?"

"Asking a fellow what colour pants he'll be wearing. Just seems a bit ... you know ... private, that's all."

"Why? I'm gonna see them when I meet you, aren't I?

"Are you?"

"Of course. And you're gonna see mine."

109

"Is ..." I was acutely aware of a reddening of the facial regions at this point, I don't mind saying. "Is that, um, normal behaviour for hereabouts?"

"Sure. Why?"

"Well, it's just that one doesn't usually do that sort of thing in England."

"What! I've seen films from England. You all do it. Hell, what else are you gonna do with pants? Hide them? Come on William, what's the point of spending a lot of money on good pants if you're not gonna let people see them?"

"Well ... I just think that ... ah ... a fellow's undergarments are ... um ... a bit of a personal ... thing. Not to be put on public display, and so forth."

"Undergarments? What are talking about?"

"Pants. Nether-region containment items. Smalls."

There was more girly laughter at that stage. "Oh, William." Even louder girly laughter. "Oh ... my ... God. Oh no wonder you thought ..." Louder still. "God, I just adore your sense of humour. Oh jeez ...you really crack me up. You are so-ooo funny."

"I am? What ... ?"

"Pants, William, pants."

"I'm still at a bit of a loss, old thing."

"What you call trousers, we call pants ... or slacks."

"Oh! Ah ... yes. Of course. Ha-ha. Oh dear. You thought that I thought that you thought that I meant ... Ha-ha, yes, indeed."

"Your British humour is just so-ooo dry. Do you think it's dry?"

"Positively arid."

"Anyway, I think the best place for us to meet is right outside the thee-ay-ter. It's the San Francisco Opera House. Do you know where that is?"

"You mentioned something about Van Ness."

110

"That's right, it's on Van Ness ... Opposite City Hall. Do you know where I mean?"

"I think so. The place that looks a bit like St Paul's cathedral in London."

"What does?"

"City Hall."

"That's right. Although we would say it was looks more like St Peter's basilica, in Rome."

"An easy mistake to make."

"So, all you have to do is take the cable-car to Powell Street, then get the BART to Civic Centre, take the Grove Street exit and walk three blocks. Is that okay?"

"Sounds fine to me."

"Great. See you there."

"Yes. Oh ... what time?"

"It starts at eight ... so I guess we could meet at ... what? Seven-thirty."

"Seven-thirty it is."

"Great. See you then."

"Yes."

To say that my mind was in a bit of a confused state when I finished the call would be putting it mildly. Spinning and seemingly inside an exploding rainbow – lots of sparkling colours and blurred edges and so forth – would be nearer the mark. And for why? I asked myself. What could possibly happen?

The Opera with Ron.

I arrived at the entrance to the San Francisco Opera house at seven-fifteen. Not because I wanted to be early – not that fifteen minutes ahead of schedule could be described as early; unless you were making love, I would imagine - but because I didn't know the times of the cable-cars and BART trains. Furthermore, hanging around train stations has never really been high on my list of attractions – especially in foreign cities – and then having to take multiple detours to avoid thinking of excuses not to dole out all my loose change to the plethora of land-loupers and mendicants that are to be found congregating at the subway exits.

I made my way along Grove Street, taking time to admire City Hall, then across Van Ness (reputed to be the widest street in San Francisco) and up the steps of the Opera House. On my way, I almost went, by mistake, into a very imposing building that was nearby; curved at the front, with a lot of blue glass windows and – and this was very strange – there was a huge plaque on the front that appeared to have been dedicated to a great seal. Actually, it was *the* great seal of California. Rather odd thing to commemorate, I have to say: perhaps it made a guest appearance when Leese and Primer held their celebration party: perhaps it was on the menu.

Most peculiar; but there again, it was San Francisco. In the end, I decided that it might have been one that had descendants amongst those lounging down near pier 39. Maybe I'll get to see them sometime.

But what a marvellous building the Davies Symphony Hall is. Plenty of curves and glass. I wasn't entirely sure what the blobs of stone at the front were meant to represent, but I suppose that anything by Henry Moore is worth a quick feel. Yorkshire lads seem to get everywhere!

Anyway, back to the Opera House. After a quick look up at the loggia and its columns and balustrade, I popped up the steps and wandered about for a while, weaving in and out of the many opera buffs, and marvelling at the range of accents and topics from the conversations that I overheard.

But oh dear: the number of people with mobile phones: and I don't mean just there. It seemed that almost everybody in San Francisco owns a mobile phone, and feels an overwhelming urge to constantly use it. I was forever seeing people walking along the pavements with a phone either stuck to their ear, or hidden about their person and connected to their ear by means of a wire. With the latter, it was a bit disconcerting for a while to go past so many people who appeared to be deep in conversation with somebody who wasn't there. I began to wonder if there was something in the local water that conjured up thousands of 'Harveys', and how long it would be before mine appeared.

But, dash it all, people would even be using their mobile phone when walking beside someone else! I mean to say, how rude is that? I cannot help feeling that I would have raised an objection within a very few strides. I'm sure that a sharp jab in the ribs with the pointed end of an umbrella would quickly restore the necessary etiquette.

The use of the mobile phone, however, wasn't confined to the sidewalk: it was also very prevalent on buses, tubes, cinemas, and even at restaurant tables. I don't know about you, but I have always been under the impression that using a mobile phone whilst in company is to be regarded as something of a pretty poor show. To use it at a restaurant table is about as insulting as one can be without making a disparaging remark about their hair. At least it would have been had not some of the male phone users still been wearing their hats.

Of course, I say 'hats', but often the excuses on some heads were little short of a sock or a piece of cloth with a duck's bill attached to it. On top of which, some of the wearers were quite obviously unsure of which way round the head covering was supposed to be pointing. Perhaps the items were sold without any form of instruction.

Further, to return to the subject of mobile phone calls, it wasn't as though the calls were of the utmost importance. I could understand the need to use the phone if I heard comments like ... "I'll do the operation as soon as I get to the hospital," or "Don't mention the take-over to anybody else." Maybe even "Make sure the president doesn't push any buttons until I get there."

But that was never the case. The most common collection of words usually ran along the lines of ... "I'm on the bus," "Where are you now?" and "I'm looking over there, but I can't see you. Can you wave?" Prosaic in the extreme. But the most extraordinary, and downright asinine, one I heard was at a theatre to which I later went - "The curtain's going up now." Doesn't that make you feel really proud to share a common ancestry?

Since my return to the UK, however, I have noticed a similar increase in the numbers of mobile phones, and the use of those 'Bluetooth' contraptions that always look as though the user has some kind of unfortunate growth on the side of their head that really ought to be surgically removed. But what about the sort of individual using them? You know the type I mean - people who look as though they were probably in the wrong queue when intelligence was being dispensed. We've all seen them, as they wander through shopping malls with a communication device stuck to the side of their face, awaiting that 'oh-so-urgent' call: invariably from their mother telling them not to forget the milk.

You will be pleased to read that I am not going to start on the numbers of car drivers that I saw in San Francisco who seemed unable to put down their phones: maybe they wanted to maintain an 'open' line in case of a crash.

Some times I do yearn for a return to the days when telephone boxes had an 'A' and a 'B' button: days when private phone numbers had three letters and three numbers: days when Whitehall one-two one-two meant something.

I know that, when compared to the present day, things were awfully slow, but back then you had nothing with which to compare it. So you had to go through several exchanges before your phone call got connected ... So what? To be able to speak with someone in another country was simply astonishing. So your television only had a seven-inch screen, came in a wardrobe, and took half an hour to warm up ... So what? It generated

114

more excitement than anything present-day children can understand.

I can also remember – just – sitting in front of the television, anxiously waiting for 'Watch with Mother'. No doubt incredibly dull by today's standards, but back then it was magical: and clean. No smutty innuendoes, no shock content, and no damn repeats. On top of which, all the presenters knew how to enunciate properly: words still had the letter 'T' in them, and 'H' was pronounced 'aitch' and not that dreadful 'haitch' that seems so widespread these days. And, when they didn't have anything of merit to broadcast, they used to show a test-card or someone working away at a potter's wheel. Hardly riveting it has to be said, but enormously calming all the same.

Those were days when broadcasting closed down between eleven and twelve at night, and finished with the playing of the National Anthem. Which, incidentally, they also used to play in cinemas at the end of the film: and people stood whilst it was played. These days, the only time respect is shown it is usually accompanied by one of those silly 'gang' hand gestures that involve fingers pointing in different directions. Dear, oh dear.

Whilst on the subject of television, I should like to draw your attention to one or two peculiarities of televisual treats to be found in America.

Don't get me wrong; over the years, I have watched quite a lot of American television programmes that I enjoyed. One or two of the newer 'sit-coms', and my mind occasionally goes back to the days of 'I love Lucy', 'Greenacres', and the 'Beverley Hillbillies'. I still remember lines such as ...

"Greenacres is the place to be,
  Farm living is the life for me,
    Land spreadin' out so far and wide,
      Something, something, give me that countryside."

However, until I watched television in San Francisco, I never realised just how much modern-day American television is dominated by advertisements. So many in fact, that there were many occasions when I was unsure if I was still watching the actual programme. I could just about manage to notice if the 'news' was interrupted by someone telling me to buy a used car; but run-of-the-mill programmes seemed to merge seamlessly with various people promoting various products. The hero would just be about to dispose of the bad guy when he would turn to the camera and tell the viewers about a really good way to stop their drains from smelling.

But even being able to spot the joins in the 'news' programmes didn't quite spare me from the shock of being told, by the presenter, that the programme had been 'brought' to me by the manufacturers of 'Rubbiton' haemorrhoid cream. Perhaps there was meant to be a hidden message there concerning what people are usually told by the media, and I simply didn't fathom it. Who knows?

But what about the obligation (either legal or moral, I wasn't sure) to tell us all about all the side-effects of a particular type of merchandise – you can choose from virtually anything that is meant to be swallowed, rubbed on, or worn – that might include headache, sore throat, and, in the case of a certain type of hair gel, nosebleeds. You do begin to wonder what goes into these products: but then, remembering that tobacco has more than nine hundred 'extras' shoved in, perhaps I shouldn't enquire.

There was also a glut of advertisements on how to avoid ageing. Perhaps people should take a leaf from the writings of Rabindranath Tagore when he mentioned something about Death's stamp giving value to the coin of Life. You could add, by way of a little seasoning, a dash of 'Pereunt et Imputantur'. People spend so much time doing things to slow ageing and prolong life, and then forget to do anything with the extra time they gain.

However, my favourite was an advertisement for a particular tablet that was intended to combat arthritis. The plus point for the medication was that it would enable you overcome joint pain, so you could get up and dance. The downside was that it might cause diarrhoea. Just the thing you want to risk happening when you get up and dance! Mind you, it would make for terrific (literal sense) viewing.

If I may return to the subject of overheard conversations for a moment, I would like to cite some that I managed to catch (well, they were so loud I had little chance of avoiding them) whilst I passed people who were walking and talking - without the use of a telephone. Examples that, I suspect, one might not hear in other parts of the world.

In the UK one will often catch snippets about the weather, the previous evening's television programmes, what a particular pop singer might be up to, or something to do with football. In San Francisco ...

"He's got a atta-tood problem. He's got friends ... he should relate to them."

"She's real ant-eye social."

"I ain't gonna put none o'dat super-shit on it ... I's goin' for da reg'lar perm."

"You ain't gonna bleed me. I know d'jou, cos' I live wid d'jou."

"You ain't getting' my ass, you black mother: not my ass you ain't."

But I feel that the strangest has to be -

"Did you hear about Angelo?" ... "No." ... "He got hit bad by a catfish."

Anyway, enough reverie: I was on the lookout for Ron. He had said that, as driving a car in the City was tantamount to ordering a nervous breakdown, he too would be arriving by BART; so I kept my eyes on the Grove Road approach.

I think I saw the powder-blue jacket about five minutes before I actually got to meet Ron. Like a shard of clear sky as he

... I was going to say walked, but I think 'sashayed' might be more accurate: and certainly more polite than 'minced'. However, I shall settle for 'made' his way up the steps to where I was standing.

He was indeed a vision: resplendent in a black turtleneck sweater, a lightweight powder–blue jacket, shiny black trousers, shiny red silk handkerchief in his jacket breast pocket, and grey suede shoes. I wasn't sure about the handbag type of thing he was carrying, though, but I managed to keep my eyebrows in check.

As well as the above, Ron had dark hair with gold-coloured streaks in it, and a beard and moustache that were so neat and well-trimmed that they could have been painted on.

"William," he exclaimed, raising his hands as he weaved between the other theatre-goers. "How simply wonderful to meet you."

"Yes," I coughed in an attempt to deepen my voice. "Likewise, I'm sure." I offered my right hand on the end of a rigid, and very straight, right arm - in case Ron had it in mind to give me a hug. It turned out to be a wise move as I was then, quite literally, able to keep Ron at arm's length while he tried to manoeuvre himself into a position where he could throw his arms round me.

I have never liked the continental way of greeting people: especially if they are members of my own sex. As far as I am

118

concerned, hugs should be reserved for the ladies with whom one either has a blood or marital link. I also think, as one sees the years in one's account dwindling away, that one should make strenuous efforts to avoid becoming one of those unpleasant old men who seem to kiss and hug women (especially young women) on the excessive side of acceptable. I am sure that you recognise the gentlemen, often uncles, to whom I refer.

So, after a few moments of a rather bizarre dance where I would, keeping my right arm locked and my right hand tightly gripping Ron's, move a few steps to the right, followed by a few more to the left - in order to prevent him from smothering me in a cuddle that I knew was normally kept for other wearers of powder-blue jackets - we tacitly agreed to keep our welcome to one that would have been acceptable in any gentleman's club.

"My," Ron then said, his eyes widening, "haven't you got a strong grip."

"Ah ... yes ... hmm," I replied, my voice dropping to a level that would have made Paul Robeson seem like a castrato. "Quite."

"Did you have any problems getting here?"

"No. Your instructions were spot on. Thank you."

"Oh great. Now ..." Ron said, as he looked from side to side. "Do you think we have time for a drink before we take our seats?"

I looked at my watch. "I expect so."

"Wonderful. Come on then. Follow me."

So off we went. Ron in front and occasionally waggling his fingers at acquaintances of his, whilst I, desperately trying to move like a cross between Clint Walker and Bill Kazmaier, followed behind; my hands firmly clasped behind my back in case Ron tried to lead me by one of them.

At this point I feel it advisable to stress that I am not homophobic. Not simply, as I may have mentioned on a previous occasion, because I have always felt that 'phobic' is a bit of a misnomer. A phobia – to my way of thinking, as, now I think a bit more, I *know* I have mentioned before – is an intense and irrational fear and, as such, is not the point. I am not frightened of homosexuals. I just don't like what they do: it doesn't seem natural to me. And before any of you 'activist' types begin leaping up and down shouting things about how I ought to be more tolerant, I'll add the fact that I will defend their right to do what they want - providing it's consential and in the privacy of their own homes. I will, however, firmly decline any offers to go along and watch. It's simply not my 'thing'. To me, the sight of two men holding hands just looks .... wrong. Alas, one doesn't get a lot of choice in the matter in certain parts of San Francisco.

This situation, so I am led to believe, came about as a result of the military purging suspected homosexuals at their point of embarkation during the Second World War. This meant that those expecting to serve in the Pacific war zone got pushed out of the services in San Francisco and, being unable to face the stigma of a return back to their homes, they simply stayed. Ever since, the city became something of a refuge for people of similar inclinations.

Although, if truth be told, it had been known, amongst the prospectors and merchants who came to the Barbary Coast to seek their fortunes during the early gold-rush days, that, in the saloons and dancehalls catering to them, a bandana worn around their arm meant that they wished to be led in a dance. Over time, the 'hanky code' evolved into quite a complex symbolic language that came to involve, amongst other things, bunches of keys that were displayed from certain pockets. In fact, the first bar that openly catered to patrons who preferred to play for the other team was in full swing (if you'll pardon the expression) at Pacific and Kearney as far back as 1908.

Back to my initial remark ... am I homophobic? I think the simple answer to that is no. Have I read the Book of Leviticus? Yes. Am I going to quote extracts from it? No. Was I feeling uncomfortable about being with Ron? Slightly: but more of that later.

Anyway, to return to my present whereabouts, I followed Ron up several flights of stairs inside the Opera House which, I have to say, is a spectacular building. Designed by Arthur Brown Jnr, the doors opened for its first production back in October 1932, when they put on Tosca. I believe the place got something called a 'Seismic Retrofit' back in 1989 – as a result of damage suffered during the Loma Prieta earthquake – and now seats around 3,200 people. I can't say that I have any knowledge of buildings that is really worth mentioning, but I do know when I like something: and I like the San Francisco Opera House - or the War Memorial Opera House as it is often called. Actually, I have a feeling - if the letters carved in the façade are anything to go by - that might well be its official name.

Ron and I paused at one of the bars on the way up to take our seats and partook of a small libation. I opted for an 'eau de vie' in the form of a whisky and water (in keeping with one of my favoured tastes and, coincidentally, with the macho image I was endeavouring to engender), whilst Ron ordered something that sounded like a cow's loo and cream.

Conversation at this point was difficult due to the surrounding cacophony that assailed my organs of hearing, so I took the opportunity to do a little bit of people watching. I, like many others I suspect, have always felt that one ought to dress in accordance with the occasion and its location.

However, to show the antithesis of such etiquette, two instances spring to mind. The first was when our then Prime Minister turned up at the Queen Mother's State Funeral – back in 2002 – wearing a lounge suit: having, so I believe, been asked by the Palace to wear morning attire. As for the way his wife 'chasmously' yawned during the service, and on several other official engagements ... Well, decorum wasn't the first word that sprang to mind! The second was when his chancellor went to make a Mansion House speech and turned up in a plain brown suit. Had I been working on the door that day, I would have pointed out that he was in breach of the dress code and turned him away: and in pretty quick order I can tell you.

Anyway, black tie for dinner parties, lounge suits for cocktail parties, and whatever you fancy for fancy-dress parties. The opera, I have always felt, has usually required that one turns up in formal wear: but, of late, I have taken to understand that one should, at the very least, be wearing a shirt and tie. I was, therefore, saddened to see quite a few people who felt – especially as the venue was the San Francisco Opera House - that it was either clever or acceptable to arrive in clothes that would have been better suited for wearing whilst washing one's car. Or maybe those concerned were just too stupid to realise their faux pas. Back to the Alhambra v. the Allotment situation I suppose: more is the pity.

But all that aside, we soon took our seats for Turandot. Then came the first of two surprises. When the curtain went up, we were treated to a set that had been designed by David Hockney. I have to admit to knowing next to nothing about the gentleman, or his previous endeavours, but I was able to appreciate the fact that the set was splendid. Not quite as lavish as one I had seen (on video, I hasten to add) under the production of Franco Zeffirelli – performed at the Metropolitan Opera House, New York, back in 1987 – but spectacular nonetheless. So, hats off and a round of applause for that.

The second surprise came when ... This might be a good moment to ask if you are familiar with the story of Turandot. For those who are not, I'll elaborate. Briefly.

It is set in Peking - where the Imperial Palace houses Princess Turandot - for whose hand many suitors come to risk their lives by trying to answer three questions. Get one wrong and your head is removed from your body. Result to date – Living suitors 0 : Lost heads 6. Latest unsuccessful applicant – the Prince of Persia.

Enter Liu (slave girl), Timur (her aged master), and Calaf (Timur's son, for whom Liu has rather a soft spot). Turandot appears, orders removal of Persian Prince's head, and is spotted by Calaf - who falls in love with her, and throws his hat in the ring.

Three of Turandot's ministers (Ping, Pang and Pong) try, unsuccessfully, to dissuade Calaf from attempting the questions; but Calaf remains resolute. Then there's a big scene as Turandot fires the questions — positively licking her lips at the thought of another execution — but, surprise, surprise, Calaf answers them correctly. I shan't tell you what they are as I don't want to spoil the story for you. Mind you, if it's being sung in Italian and your translatory skills are on a par with mine, I don't suppose it will make much difference anyway.

Having said that, quite a few operas houses have 'sur-titles' these days - a sort of moving words in some version of an LED thing that hangs over the stage. Most ingenious, I have to say. Others, the Vienna Opera House for one, have little screens in front of each seat. All very helpful, but one tends to be reading quite a lot of the time, and maybe missing a bit of the essence of the show. Although I have noticed that certain opera houses tend to switch off the words when a good part of the singing happens along. As when Cio-Cio-San has the telescope stuck to her eye and hits some of the big notes in 'Un Bel Di', or when old Tosca has a bit of writhe on the floor whilst warbling her tonsils with 'Visi d'Arte'.

But back to Turandot: when the answers from Calaf come in, Turandot looks shaken and tries to renege on the contract. Her father (Emperor Altoum) won't hear of it, Turandot panics, so Calaf offers her a 'get out' by generously offering her a challenge of her own. If she can learn his name by dawn, he will forfeit his life. Turandot accepts, and Calaf reckons he can't loose: but Turandot has a scheme up her sleeve.

She proclaims that, on pain of death, nobody in Peking gets to enjoy forty winks until she learns the stranger's name. Cue 'Nessun Dorma'. Soldiers drag in Liu and Timur, intent on 'encouraging' them to spill the beans ... Liu says she is the only one who knows the name and then kills herself to protect Calaf. Crowd goes off to bury Liu, Calaf – alone with Turandot for the first time – kisses her and releases her emotions, and the two rush off to get married. Simple as that.

Or at least it should have been. Now, allowing for the fact that the story does enjoy a dash of licence, I think the audience was being asked to stretch its imagination a tad too far when Turandot first walked onto the stage.

Bearing in mind that we (the audience) were expected to believe that suitors from all corners of the world were prepared to toddle along and risk their necks (literally) in their attempts to win the hand of Turandot, it would have added a certain amount of plausibility had said princess been a real stunner. You know the sort of thing – looks that make you gasp. Well, Turandot certainly had looks that made you gasp: just not sure it was in quite the way that Giacomo P had in mind when he was writing. Or maybe the suitors had only read her profile in the local 'lonely hearts' columns; and we all know how accurate some of those can be! I say 'we', but, obviously, I am only going by what I have heard from other people. Naturally.

Anyway, whatever the cause of the misunderstanding, on she came. I'm not sure if I can adequately describe the collective sound that emanated from the audience when Turandot made her initial appearance, but it was a good deal more than 'barely discernable'. If I estimated the weight of Turandot to have been in the region of 400 lbs I would probably be erring on the light side of things. She was colossal. Huge. Well, certainly not the svelte Chinese princess that one might have been expecting.

Soon after she started treating us to her diaphragmatic prowess, some rather odd things began happening: that is to say, I was aware of some unscheduled asides and several mistimed entrances by the fellows playing Turandot's ministers. First Ping would appear, look around a bit sheepishly, glance at the conductor, shrug his shoulders and then wander off again. This exercise was repeated a couple more times; and then Pang and

Pong started doing the same thing. Then all three came on together, with rather quizzical looks on their faces. It was about then I noticed one or two of the cast had started ducking from time to time; and then someone in the chorus shrieked out, clasped her right eye and ran from the stage.

Astute members of the audience were now realising that the production was straying a touch from the original, and were beginning to wonder if Mr Hockney had thought of a new angle. Several theories were no doubt under construction when it became apparent that certain sections of Turandot's costume were coming adrift. It seemed that the reason for the confusion was due to several buttons being put under unsustainable pressure and subsequently getting propelled in various directions, and the sound they made was responsible for the ministers thinking that they had been summoned. All of which was great fun, it has to be said.

On top of that, I have a feeling that the initial impact of Turandot in all her finery might well have been offset slightly by wondering if the production team had maybe asked her to remain on the more robust parts of the set.

But putting all of that aside, I would like to be the first one to say that she had a magnificent voice, and her rendition of 'Del Primo Pianto', as if by some unseen bind of sympathy, very nearly moved me to tears. Splendid stuff all round.

125

The bit, however, that I did find somewhat less moving was when Turandot asked Calaf, who had by then won the bet, if he 'would hold her in his arms by force; reluctant, quivering'.

Excuse me? I couldn't imagine The Incredible Hulk would have been able to hold her in his arms 'by force' if she didn't want to be there. I also felt that he would have had some difficulty in getting his arms around her in the first place. And had she started with the quivering bit ... Well, a rather rapid evacuation of the premises might have been called for.

Then my imagination began to conjure up thoughts of what might happen if said diva ever got round to playing Tosca. Two images came to the forefront: both concerning the final scene when Tosca, in deep sorrow at the death of her beloved Cavaradossi, throws herself off the castle battlements.

Firstly, how on earth would she have got up there in the first place? Secondly, I dread to think of the carnage that would surely occur as a result of her hitting the stage floor. Another orderly evacuation being in order no doubt, with people wondering if the 'Big One' had finally arrived.

And that brought to mind two anecdotes (whose veracity I cannot confirm, but I don't think it really matters as they are quite funny) in connection with productions of Tosca. The first concerned a particular Prima Donna who had been aggravating most of the cast and production crew, for the entire run. On the last night, it was decided to play a wee prank on the source of all the irritation, and a well-disguised trampoline was placed at the spot where Tosca was due to land after her leap. The result, so I understand, was spectacular and ameliorated all the previous displeasures.

Tosca, it is told, sang out her last words – kindly informing dear old Scarpia that God would be their judge – before throwing herself off the battlements: and then bouncing back into view again. Twice. Not, I suspect, quite the effect that Puccini had in mind, but well worth the admission fee.

126

The second was reputed to have taken place in Australia when a particular company was touring over there. All was going well with the tour when, just before the last performance, there was a strike by one of the actors' unions. Not sure which one, but it didn't affect the principals – as they didn't belong to it – just the 'extras'.

One of the groups involved in the walkout was the men who played the part of the firing squad that was due to shoot Cavaradossi. The director, not wanting the production to be spoiled, went to the local army barracks and recruited six of their finest to play the part. So far so good. Except for the fact that the soldiers didn't know anything about the opera.

"No problem," said the producer. "When given the signal, shoot Cavaradossi, wait for a moment, and then leave the stage after Tosca."

Simple enough instructions, one would have thought. However, on the night, the final scene came along and the soldiers received their instruction to shoot Cavaradossi. Again, one has to say, a fairly simple instruction; but one of the firing squad was heard to ask, "Which one's Cavaradossi?"

"Dunno mate," replied the soldier next to him. "That fella over there, I think."

Net result was that one of the jailers got shot, Cavaradossi (who was standing on another part of the stage) fell to the ground, and Tosca, grieving loudly, jumped over the castle wall ... and was immediately followed by the entire firing squad.

But, to return to Turandot, the show really was wonderful.

<u>Swimming is such fun.</u>

Another sun-filled morning found me casually strolling in an area that is known as Aquatic Park – having got there by hopping on the Powell-Hyde cable-car. Am I beginning to sound a bit like of a local?

"I hopped on the cable-car and flashed my fast pass." Hmm; that does have a certain cachet to it, wouldn't you say? Next thing you know I'll start wishing "Y'all have a nice day." Hmm.

And, may I say, how close Alcatraz seems when you're descending the last part of Hyde Street. Almost as if you could reach out and touch it, and, strangely enough, a lot closer than it looked from sea level. I'm quite sure it is all due to some optical illusion or other – probably caused by the intervening stretch of water and atmospheric diffraction I expect. Something well outside my range of understanding, anyway.

On the way down, the conductor fellow gave some quip about the 'Next street on the right is the crookedest street in the USA. Apart from Wall Street! Ha-ha-ha.' I expect he says that every time he passes Lombard Street, but he didn't look as though he was growing tired of the banter. Although, I am under the impression that a certain Snake Alley in Burlington (Iowa) might argue about the accuracy of his statement.

He also passed a comment about the steepness of same: and it certainly was a touch on the slanty

128

side of comfortable: especially if you happened to walking up it at the time. But, I hasten to add – and bring to your attention the extent of my research capabilities – the stretch of Filbert Street between Leavenworth and Hyde is probably the steepest of them all. Somewhere around about a 1:3 slope, or, for those who prefer degrees to ratios, 31·5 degrees. However, if competition floats your boat, I ought to further bring to your attention a certain Baldwin Street in Dunedin (New Zealand) that boasts a 1:2·27; and that translates as a slope of 38 degrees.

Here's something I hadn't thought about until just now – the trouble I had trying to get the decimal points (in the above ratio examples) to appear where they are instead of just as a full stop as seems to be the common practice these days. When did the decimal point move? It would have been nice to have told.

Back to the sloped streets. I should imagine that anyone who deals in car brakes and clutches in San Francisco is unlikely to fall upon hard times: unlike, presumably, a purveyor of children's prams. Apparently, 'hill starts' and parking with wheels facing the kerb form a large part of the driving test in these parts; hardly surprising, I suppose.

Anyway, there I was, strolling along the front near the start of a stretch they call Fisherman's Wharf, admiring the paddle-steamer, ocean-going tug, schooners and the three-masted steel-hulled ship that were moored alongside the Hyde Street Pier. It really does warm the old cockles to know that there are, amongst the hordes of philistines who run around on this planet, people who want to preserve such beautiful vessels. Okay, they're not as fast as modern-day craft, or as technically equipped; but they're way out in front in the romance stakes. Almost made me want to dance the Hornpipe, I don't mind admitting: and I may well have, had I known how to perform said jig.

Mind you, I'm not sure those in the vicinity would have been all that thrilled to see a fellow of my years look as though he was having some kind of a fit. Especially at that time of the day. Can be quite unsettling for those of a particular disposition, you know.

I continued with my promenade, and soon noticed a couple of bods in the water. One's first reaction at such times is to shout loudly to see if assistance is required, and then strip off and plunge in if that proves to be the case. However, on that particular day, I had a touch of the bronchials and didn't think that my broadcast would have reached the unfortunates. Fearing the worst, especially if the rumours of the local water temperature proved to be founded, I looked around to see if I could attract attention in another fashion.

Nothing was close to hand, so I dashed towards a rather corpulent gentleman who was approaching and voiced my concerns. They were to prove groundless.

"Nah ..." began the rather nasal reply. "Them's swimmers. Probably just swurm in frarm Alcatraz."

"Good heavens," I said, unable to hide my surprise. "I didn't realise it was still a working establishment."

"Her-whut?"

"That it was currently in use as a place of penal rectitude."

"Her-whut?"

"That it was still a prison."

"Listen, buddy, I'm saying they's doin' a pleasure swee-yim. Do it on a reg'lar basis."

"A pleasure swee ... Swim. Oh! But I thought that was impossible. All the currents, and the cold; and those rather large, and usually predatory, fish."

"The her-whut?"

"Sharks. Isn't the Bay supposed to be full of them? Rather tiresome if you fancied a quick dip, I should have thought."

"Nah ... those guys keep purdy dee-yip."

"They keep ... But they are out there, nonetheless."

"Sure. Sometimes. But ah cain't recall the last times someone got eat bah one."

"Not even a nibble?"

"Them fellas keeps to themselves. They're say-end sharks."

"Say-end?"

"Say-end. They live down on the say-end."

"Oh, the sand. Right."

"Why? You fancy having a go?"

"At living on the sand?"

"No. Doing the swee-yim."

"Good lord, no!"

"No? Say, are you British?"

"Yes, yes indeed."

"Yeller?"

"Excuse me?"

"You fry-tend of doin' the swe-yim?"

"Fry ...? Frightened? Of course not. Just rather keen on keeping my limbs, and all their attendant digits, at the present number."

"Like I sayed, ain't no-one lost no flesh that I cain recall. So maybe you's a mite scurred. Huh?"

"Was the double negative intended?"

"The her-whut?"

"Was the ... Oh never mind."

"So ... is yer doin' it or not?"

"Doing what?"

"The swee-yim. The Alcatraz swee-yim."

"No, of course not."

"So you is yeller."

"I most certainly am not yellow. Nor, I might add, any other colour associated with a flaw in one's character. I just happen to be the possessor of an above-average helping of common sense."

"That sounds like yeller to me. British ... huh!"

131

It was at that point I felt an overwhelming desire to administer a clenched fist to the end of the gentleman's nose. It is bad enough to be accused of a slight hesitancy to put oneself in a situation that may cause injury by a person who speaks English with an accent that even Slim Pickens would have disowned; but to be accused of pusillanimity by someone who looked as if they thought a good and meaningful life should consist of consuming copious amounts of popcorn and cola whilst debating issues as important as the relative standards of the National and the American baseball leagues, was a mite beyond the pale.

"Now look here, sir," I said, as the strains of Elgar's Pomp and Circumstance began to materialise within my consciousness, "I rather take exception to your attitude."

"You her-whut?"

"I said … that I rather take exception to your attitude."

"And what in the hail does that me-yun?"

"It means … Oh, I'm sorry, is English not your first language?"

"Ah speak American."

"Well, I suppose that we all have a cross to bear."

"Uh?"

"Oh dear."

I was about to fire a witticism at the poor fellow regarding the differences between inflections and infections of the English language, when I realised the futility of the exercise: it would probably have cleared the top of his head with several feet to spare.

"So her-whut? You're still yeller, whatever language ah use."

"I most certainly am not."

"Then why doan you pur-roove it."

"Purr - How?" I asked, having more than an inkling that a reasoned debate with all the correlated premises and conclusions might have proved a tad ambitious.

"By doin' that swee-yim."

"What! The Alcatraz swim?"

"Sure."

"Oh. Well, of course, I would, only ... Only you probably have to be a member of something. I expect."

"Why?"

"Because ... because of insurance and ... such things. I know how much you Americans enjoy gratuitous litigation and the like."

"Bool-she-yit. You jest ain't got the bawls fawah eeit."

My mind started being bombarded with two sets of thoughts. The first - and the one that I decidedly wanted to favour - centred on principles concerning discretion, the better part of valour, and common sense. The second consisted entirely of wanting to take the gentleman's implications and shove them somewhere particularly uncomfortable. But before I was able to let my better judgement swallow my pride – and with images of Drake, Nelson, and Churchill pushing each other for the front position in my mind – I accepted the challenge.

"Well, okay then," I said. "Put my name down."

"Her-whut!"

"I said all right. I'll do the swim."

"You mean ... the ... You're gonna do it?"

"Certainly."

"Well ah'll be a sonovagun. Hey!"

"Hey indeed."

Whilst I then tried to comprehend what it was that I had agreed to do, my companion beckoned me to follow him, and I was shown to a brace of ramps that led to, respectively, the Dolphin and the South End clubs. A quick glance at the first notice informed me that the Dolphin Club allowed non-members in on Mondays, Wednesdays and Fridays; and the South End likewise on Tuesdays, Thursdays and Saturdays. The order being reversed at the start of the following, and succeeding months. And, as it was a Wednesday, I was invited to tug on the bell belonging to the Dolphin Club.

133

My initial cheer that nobody seemed interested in responding to my request for ingress was dampened when, after about a minute, the door opened. My disappointment was exacerbated when I noticed that the gentleman who opened the door was missing one of his hands. The left one to be exact. Although, to be perfectly honest, I don't think it would have made any difference had it been the right one: the sharks appeared to be active.

"Yes?" the mono-mitted man enquired.

"I ... ah ... um ..."

"This guy – he's British – would like to do the Alcatraz swee-yim," offered my companion. "Reckons he can do ut."

"Oh. I see. Have you swum here before?"

"No," I replied, detecting a slight, and probably distant, connection with the British Isles in the man's voice.

"Never mind, new swimmers are always welcome."

"Oh. Good."

"My name's Peter, by the way."

"Pleased to meet you, Peter. I'm William."

"Hi, William."

"There yer go, buddy," offered my fleshy companion. "Told yer there'd be no prob-layem."

"So you did. And that was very decent of you."

"Let me know when ya do it, huh. Here's ma card." With that, he thrust a business card into my top pocket. "You have a good one, y'hear."

"I shall certainly endeavour to," I replied, as he turned and walked away; chortling.

I checked the card: the fellow went by the name of Weiden Spinkbuttock and had an address on one of the avenues in the Sunset district of the City. *Weiden Spinkbuttock*! I'm not sure that I really have any reason to make further comment – but I shall anyway. *Spink*buttock Hmm. I wasn't entirely sure about the origin of that cognomen. *Vast*buttock I could have understood.

Peter then invited me inside the Dolphin Club and within ten minutes I had been shown around the premises, whilst receiving an abridged history. I was also told why the Dolphin Club was so much better than the South End Club. Reasons, I was later to discover, that exactly — although coming from a different direction - matched those offered by the South End Club.

"Is this your first visit to the City?" Peter asked, when we returned to the lounge area.

"Yes, it is."

"How are you enjoying it?"

"It's early days, but so far no real problems. Unless you count that rather unpleasant gentleman who was here earlier."

"Yes, he was a bit offensive, wasn't he?"

"Indeed. Tell me, Peter," I asked, "do I detect the vestiges of a British lilt to your voice?"

"Uh-huh. Mind you, it's been a while since I last lived there. Back in sixty-nine."

"I expect the old place has changed somewhat since then."

"You can say that again. Sure, I return from time to time, but it's with less enthusiasm each trip."

"Why is that?"

"I usually stay in London — on business. But it's not the London I used to know. Back then you had to look carefully to find a foreigner. These days it's the other way round. Hard to tell if you're in Kampala, Krakow or Kensington."

I quite understood, and concurred with, Peter's sentiments.

"Like you say, William, it was a sure different world. Good manners seem to have dwindled away to virtually nothing; and people don't have any respect for anybody. Heck, I can remember having to make an appointment to go see the bank manager and feeling real scared about it. The guy wore a stiff collar, and just oozed status and dignity. But these days … Jeez."

Perhaps that was why we had to wear detached collars at school. The blooming trouble I used to have with those studs:

especially on cold winter mornings when the old fingers weren't always quite as nimble as they should have been. Mind you, I did master the Shelby tie knot: and, yes, I do mean the one where you start with the seam of the tie facing outwards. Always the one to use when you prefer a small, triangular knot.

"Although," I ventured, "a lot of those in charge of banks haven't exactly been playing with a straight bat of late, have they?"

"That's true enough. But, hey, enough melancholia," Peter continued. "What brings you to these shores?"

"Rather a bizarre story, actually. I won a competition I didn't enter."

"Novel."

"A niece and nephew to thank."

"Handy way of paying for the trip!"

"Absolutely."

"And why the desire to do the Alcatraz swim?"

"If you'd asked me about half an hour ago, I didn't even know it could be done. But not being able to let some objectionable article chide the character of those who hail from the Old Country - casting aspersions about the existence of one's spinal column and so forth - I felt obliged to hold up the British end. And then got coerced into saying I'd try it."

"Have you done any sea swimming before?"

"None. Actually, that's not quite true. I did a bit off the Isle of Wight once."

"Well, the water here is colder."

"How much colder?"

"A lot colder. No Gulf Stream. Just the waters of the north Pacific."

"Which are ...?"

"About 55 degrees."

"Good old Fahrenheit, I presume."

"We don't use that centigrade nonsense over here. Or kilometres. Or litres. Good old miles and gallons."

136

A few minutes were then spent extolling the virtues of the Imperial units against those ghastly metric monstrosities. How nice it was, as it had been ever since I arrived in the U.S., to hear people talking in units that made sense. Apart from the fact that you have to think of whether you mean a Queen Anne gallon or a Winchester gallon! And the UK gallon is about a fifth larger than the American gallon – with our system a gallon of water weighs 10 lbs (160 ozs) and so there are 160 fl ozs in a gallon, and 20 fl ozs in a pint. Thus, for the British, a fluid ounce does actually weigh an ounce. Anyway, whichever you choose, they are units that have a sense of history to them. Goodness, how I hate this creeping metrication nonsense.

If you knew the way I cringe whenever I see the weather forecasters talking about twelve millimetres of rain. What *is* that? Why not say 'half an inch'? Well, I think I know why. We're back to that fellow Monnet and his mates – a lot of whom now seem to work in the UK media. A cowardly bunch of traitors, the lot of them, if you ask me; who should be hanged at the earliest opportunity.

And what about when the television people give, for example, the pack weight of a rugby team as being 816 kilos, with an average weight of 102 kilos? How heavy is that? Say 'sixteen and half stones' and everyone knows what you're talking about.

Then we have the height fiasco. Six feet three inches ... that makes sense. One metre ninety one ... Eh? What utter nonsense! The police in the UK, so I believe, have been having all sorts of trouble issuing descriptions of felons using metric measurements. I mean to say, what does 85 kilos and 1·78 metres look like? Small wonder they're having trouble catching offenders. Mind you, having seen examples of the standard of questions asked in police entrance exams ...

Would this be a good place to talk about police targets and the appalling effect that reaching them is having on British society? Or perhaps how I think that the plan is to make the

137

British public regard our own police in such low esteem that we will welcome a European Police force with open arms? Maybe another time.

Back to measurements. I still hold with the view that the only reason we (as the UK) adopted the metric currency system (apart from being ordered to by those delightful European bureaucrats) was because the level of understanding of mathematics had fallen so much that children were having no end of trouble working out prices and change when there were twelve pennies to the shilling, and twenty shillings to the pound. In fact, it was taking young shop-assistants so long to do the arithmetic that customers were passing out from hunger while they waited to pay for their goods.

Mind you, even with the metric system, just look how long you have to wait for the correct change if the till-calculator is out of order. Have children watch a darts match during maths lessons and make them do the arithmetic in their heads is what I say. But, yet again, nobody asked me.

"So," Peter continued, "when do you fancy having a dip?"

My mind was screaming 'never', but my mouth said "How about Friday?"

"Sounds good. Come back here Friday morning ... say around ten. I'll meet you at the door. The tide'll be at slack water then. Makes it easier."

"Marvellous."

With a tentative handshake, I bade Peter goodbye and made my way back to the cable-car turn-around at the bottom of Hyde Street. Whilst waiting for the grip-man and the conductor to haul their vehicle through a hundred and eighty degrees, I should have been enjoying the guitar playing being performed by a rather lank, longhaired young man; but my mind was replaying the preceding half-hour and what I had agreed to do. The Alcatraz swim! Oh dear, oh dear.

I think the perplexed scowl on my face was responsible for the fact that I wasn't asked for my ticket, or that, despite the car being full, nobody came and sat next to me. *The Alcatraz swim!* Oh dear, oh dear, oh dear.

However, as luck would have it, we Phalaropes have been blessed with the ability to cope with crises. From the outside, we may look like gibbering wrecks when faced with dilemmas; but inside, the old grey matter is flipping through countless pages of data as it seeks to locate, and commission, the best thwartative repost to whatever quandary has chosen to hove into view.

On to my first course of action – that of how to avoid complete embarrassment. A crash fitness regime perhaps? A means of loading up the energy reserves with huge quantities of complex carbohydrates? Advertising for a doppelganger? I finally decided that my first course of action should be the acquisition of a pair of swimming trunks.

Common sense always tells me that many a scenario of acute aquatic discomfiture has been ameliorated by getting hold of suitable bathing apparel. Especially if the water happens to be on the cold side: and anyway, at 53 degrees there was certainly going to be a reduced chance of impressing the ladies.

I stayed on the cable-car all the way down to the turn-around that is located at the bottom of Powell Street – at the point where it meets Market Street. I ventured to ask the conductor where one might find a stockist of swimming garments, and was told that he thought there was a large place on the corner of Market and Fifth.

Five minutes later I was standing inside a rather imposing sports shop, known as Copeland's, and making my way to where the swimming costumes were kept. There was quite a selection: but dear me! I don't know about you, but when I go swimming I don't really want everyone else to know whether or not I am of a Jewish persuasion, or even to which side I have an inclination to dress.

I have always had a preference to wear a bathing costume that could truthfully answer to the description of 'trunks'. Not for me those slivers of cloth that barely cover one's assets; and I could not believe how sheer the materials of some of the costumes appeared. Practically see-through. As for what might happen when wet ... Doesn't bear thinking about. Call me a prude if you must, but I've always felt that unfettered visual communication with one's wedding tackle should remain within the exclusive domain of one's spouse.

I have been led to believe that the thinking behind making the material as non-existent as possible is to cut one-hundredth of a second off the time is takes for you to dash along the length of a swimming pool. But I really think the manufacturers of said garments should take into consideration that very few of us really care whether it takes 58·35 seconds, or 58·37 seconds to complete two lengths of an Olympic size swimming pool. Most people, I would venture to claim, are more concerned about not inhaling several gallons of water, as well as not exposing the contents of their gusset area to all and sundry.

I have the same sort of views about the type of clothing worn by female track and field athletes when they compete: especially when shown on television. What on earth possesses them to put on what amounts to their underwear, and then parade in front of millions of viewers? I just cannot believe that more modest clothing would make any difference whilst partaking of their chosen event. Upon further consideration, I think the reason probably lies with the television producers wanting to increase the numbers of viewers, and that semi-naked women will go a long way to achieve that end. Why not make them compete in the nude? That would surely make the figures go through the roof.

I have little doubt that some women, in order to claim their share of the limelight – and sponsor's money - would eagerly go along with it. Why have I just thought of beach volleyball? As for the male athletes who want to waggle their dangly bits for the cameras ... Once again, least said, soonest mended. I, for one, would prefer to hang onto a certain amount of personal dignity.

So, after much raising of the eyebrows and deeply furrowed frowning, I finally managed to get a shop assistant to find me a pair of trunks that fulfilled my criteria. Comfortable, robust, non see-through, held in place with a sturdy cord, and in a colour that complemented my eyes: just the job.

I try the waters.

Friday morning soon came round, rather too soon for my liking actually, and I found myself about to ding the bell to the Dolphin Club. I also found myself wishing that an earthquake might strike at that moment: just a small one, you understand, and just at that door area. But no such luck. The door opened and Peter was standing there; a wide grin on his face, as if welcoming a long-lost relative.

"William. Hi!"

"Hello. And a very good morning to you," I replied.

"All set?"

"Absolutely."

"Great. Got a costume?"

"Indeed."

"Let's go get changed."

"Yes ... let's."

Ten minutes later, I had stuffed my clothes into a visitor's locker and was following Peter down a long flight of blue wooden steps, along a wooden walkway, down a few more wooden steps, and out onto the stretch of sand (about fifty feet of it) that separated the beach doors from the Dolphin and South End Club.

I had been lent a bathing hat by another member of the Dolphin Club - apparently the cold water can affect one's brain, causing a phenomenon known as 'fridge head' – and felt a bit like Esther Williams. In fact, I half expected Ricardo Montalban to pop out from behind the fencing and sing 'Baby, it's cold outside'. And believe you me, it was. But the air temperature was positively oven-like when compared with what I felt when I put my right foot into the water. My reaction, I was later informed, upon placing said appendage into said water attracted quite a lot of attention from several startled onlookers who were enjoying a session of vigorous callisthenics in the adjacent gymnasium.

Have you ever played that game when, whilst blindfolded, you put your hand onto some ice? You know the sort of thing: your initial reaction is that it is something hot, and you pull your hand away with the vigour that results from a deep belief that your skin is being burned away. Well, such is the reaction that I underwent: only instead of it being my hand that was suddenly, and jerkily, withdrawn, it was my entire body.

I cannot be certain, you understand, as all cognitive processes seemed to shut down and then hide away under a canvas tarpaulin, but I was told that my body appeared to levitate several feet, and then leap backwards several yards; and all to the accompaniment of the type of yell that hadn't been heard in the area since some Spaniards decided to set about a few unfortunate Ohlone Indians because they didn't care for their merry indolence.

"Is everything okay?" Peter asked, as soon as it became apparent that I wasn't undergoing electro-convulsive therapy.

"Oh yes," I replied. "Splendid. Thank you."

"Not too cold, is it?"

Once again, after the initial paralysis had passed, I had visions of my childhood heroes. This time it was Scott and Shackleton.

"No, of course not. Too cold? Good lord, no. Ha!"

"Great. Come on then."

With that, Peter dived into the water and began giving as tidy a display of breaststroke of which a man with only one hand is capable. I returned to the water's edge, and with as much of a swagger as a man who firmly believes that he is about to step into liquid nitrogen can muster, I proceeded to walk into the waters of Aquatic Park.

To say that it was cold, to me at any rate, is an understatement of such magnitude that you might like to make a note of it. Or, if I may indulge in a spot of litotes, I would say that warm it wasn't. I don't think cold actually came anywhere near describing it. Freezing didn't seem to do it justice either. It felt ... Well, I say 'felt', but that would be a bit of a misnomer, as it is impossible for a foot to feel anything when it is rendered numb. And by numb, I mean frozen; anaesthetised: dead.

I was unable to feel the sand beneath my feet as I walked further in, and the numbness gave me the impression that there was somebody beneath the surface who was sawing away at my extremities, and thus creating the illusion that I was going deeper.

The men amongst you will, I am certain, empathise with the next state of affairs. Certain organs of my nether regions were now acutely aware of the advancing situation and had, seemingly, absolutely no intention of coming into contact with it. Or even close. I am sure that I was able to feel said items withdrawing from their normal locations and seeking sanctuary somewhere within the confines of my armpits.

It was about this time that my top lip decided to go into spasm, and managed to evert itself deep within my upper labial sulcus. This changed my facial appearance from that of a rather chilly Englishman into that of a dog that required urgent treatment for rabies. My breathing began to falter; and I was quite sure that my heart had thrown in the towel, packed its bags and gone off somewhere else for a well-earned rest.

My head felt warm though, and, just for a moment, I toyed with the notion of pulling my bathing hat down over the rest of my body. I resisted the temptation as I had a horrible feeling that the rubber would stretch just so far, and then spring back to its original size with a snap that might well have left me in one of those yoga positions that are normally only obtainable after several years of practice.

"Yo!" came another one of Peter's cheerful cries.

I responded with as much of a cheery wave as it was possible with arms that felt as though rigor mortis was well advanced; but I was unable to vocalise a response as my jaw muscles had decided to show me what it felt like to be suffering from trismus. Happy times indeed.

By now the water was halfway up my chest, and my gamete production facilities had arranged themselves beneath the skin above my eyebrows. I dread to think what I must have looked like – lumps on my forehead, and lips pulled back like a deranged ventriloquist's dummy.

With a final wave, and a small prayer to whichever deity had chosen to look after my affairs for that day, I struck out after the ever-diminishing form of Peter with as orthodox a front crawl stroke as I could manage under the incredible adversity that I was enduring.

I feel that this might be a good spot to bring to your attention some of the differences that I was, by now, noticing between swimming in a pool and swimming in the open sea. The temperature disparity I have already mentioned, and if I wasn't able to calculate that the numerical difference between 75 and 55 was twenty, I would have said that a drop in temperature in the region of 65 degrees might have been nearer the mark.

Then there is the wave factor. When one is on a boat, a wave height of a foot seems to be approximately twelve inches. When one is in the water, regardless of the temperature, this height seems to approach something nearer a hundred and twelve inches. Within seconds I had lost sight of Peter, the adjacent pier, the boats in the cove and, at one point, even the sky. I then lost my bearings, the use of my arms, legs, and diaphragm; and, gradually, so it seemed, the will to live.

Peter, to his credit, had, by this time, noticed that I had stopped moving in a forward direction. In fact, I believe that I had stopped moving altogether. As those of you who are au fait with the main principles involved with swimming, it is fairly essential to keep the apertures that one uses for breathing above the level of the water. Unless, of course, you are a fish. And if you were, you wouldn't be reading this, so that observation isn't really necessary.

Anyway, it transpired that my face was nowhere to be seen and, as a result, Peter had become rather concerned. I was summarily removed from the water, and placed, with the minimum of panic, back upon terra firma: and very relieved I was, I can tell you.

I have a vague recollection of being supported on either side and helped back up the wooden stairs and into the club. A moment or two later I found myself in the sauna, and my body temperature began returning to something that allowed me to move of my own free will.

"How're you feeling, William?" asked a rather troubled Peter. "Boy, did you go a funny blue colour."

"Hmm?" I replied, wondering if I was still wearing the swimming cap, or if my scalp had gone all elastic.

"That was close. Yes sir. Was that your first time in cold water?"

I managed to nod affirmatively.

"Boy, we have to get you a wet-suit."

I nodded again.

My second attempt at swimming in Aquatic Park arrived on the following Tuesday, and provided the opportunity for the South End Club to impress me with their facilities. I was armed with a wet-suit (of sorts), but still feeling rather uncertain about venturing into the icy brine for a second time.

My guide for the day was a gentleman who possessed the sobriquet Alcatraz Joe. Rather unnerving I have to say, but he turned out not to have been a former inmate of said establishment: he acquired the title as he had made the swim on several occasions and organised regular events for other people to do the same. It was beginning to seem that swimming from Alcatraz back to the mainland wasn't quite as recherché as I had originally thought. Maybe this cold-water lark wasn't as difficult to overcome as I had imagined.

Ha!

At eleven o'clock precisely, and dressed in what I can best describe as a long-sleeved T-shirt and long-johns, both made of thin black rubber, I placed my right foot into the water. It felt just as cold as it did on the Friday of the week before, but this time it wasn't quite such a shock.

"How's it goin'?" Joe asked, standing next to me in just a small costume and a blue, bobbley swim-cap.

"Marvellous," I replied through teeth that were clacking together like castanets. "Can't tell you ... how much ... I'm enjoying ... this."

"Great."

Great indeed, I thought, as I moved in up to my waist. Although expecting another migration of my gentleman's luggage, this time they appeared to be remaining in my nether whereabouts. I went in up to my neck. *Still conscious!* I took my feet off the sandy bed, and was about to congratulate myself on my progress when I discovered a salient reason for making sure that there is little or no air inside a rubber swimming outfit.

It seemed that I had, somehow, managed to allow rather a lot of air to get trapped inside my trousers when I put them on, and this ... Maybe I had better describe the trousers in a little more detail. They were made of a stretchy, rubber-like material (not dissimilar to the neoprene normally used in such underwater garments) that had a high waistband and went down the legs as far as the ankles; having tight seals at these points, which prevented the ingress of water and, consequently, the egress of air.

Not qualities that, on their own, should have caused me any difficulties: but the gentleman who had, very kindly, lent them to me was the owner of a gluteal region whose size far exceeded that owned by my good self. In fact, not to put too fine a point on it, my entire body could probably have concealed itself within the confines of one of his buttocks. This meant that, in the process of climbing into what amounted to an oversized pair of incontinence pants, I managed to trap enough air inside to allow an average-sized domestic pet to survive underwater for several hours: a situation of which I was unaware until I removed my feet from the sand.

What first brought this state of affairs to my attention was that no sooner had I relinquished contact between my plantar regions and the sand beneath them, than I noticed an extraordinary urge to invert myself. Actually, it was more than an urge: it was an irresistible force. And so, with less than an adequate degree of aplomb, I found myself floating upside down,  with my feet sticking out of the water like a pair of blanched seal flippers.

It took me several seconds to realise what had happened, and several more seconds whilst I struggled to release the trapped air from within the confines of my black rubber pantaloons.

The overall effect was not a pleasant one - either in sound or appearance - and gave the bemused onlookers an indication of what a rather thin seal suffering from really bad dyspepsia might resemble. I can only wonder at how the emerging air didn't propel me straight into one of the wooden piers.

However, equilibrium and composure were soon regained and, having adopted the nonchalant air of someone to whom such events were an everyday occurrence, I proceeded with my foray into the waters of Aquatic Park and struggled with my version of the breaststroke for a few yards.

I say 'my version', as anyone who understands these things knows that to correctly perform the breaststroke entails making both legs move horizontally – together and then apart - whilst, at some point, bending at the knee. I, however, have only been able to perform this manoeuvre with my right leg. My left one, for some reason best known to itself, prefers to move solely with an up-and-down action that is more commonly associated with the front crawl. The net result is an unattractive, and competitively disallowable, action whose use is best kept restricted to murky waters. Luckily, the waters of Aquatic Park answered that description perfectly, and I felt that further embarrassment had been avoided.

Then, feeling my confidence growing, I embarked on doing a few yards with the use of a front crawl action. This is a better stroke for me as I have always found that my limbs easily perform in the manner as laid down in *Kellerman's Guide to Correct Crawl*, and I was able to proceed with a bit more élan than I had hitherto displayed. However, what *Kellerman's Guide to Correct Crawl* had omitted to point out is that putting one's face into very cold water stimulates a phenomenon known as the Mammalian Diving Reflex.

I understand that this reflex is usually only observed during diving – I suppose that the title is a bit of a clue – but with yours truly it could clearly be observed when I merely put my face into cold water.

"What are the signs?" I hear you ask. "Pray tell."

Well, all right then. Bradycardia (a slowing down of the heart rate) is the most common sign. Except in my case it involved more than simply a 'slowing down': I would say that 'stopping' was nearer the mark. Next is Peripheral

Vasoconstriction, which is where the blood from peripheral areas starts being taken away and diverted to those parts (heart, brain and other important bits) that need it more. Then comes something that is known as Blood Shift. Here all the blood pulled from the extremities is forced into the organs of the thoracic cavity to prevent them from collapsing under the pressure. Last, but by no means least, is Apnoea – the total absence of breathing.

Quite why apnoea needs to be on the list escapes me. I should have thought that being underwater would rather get in the way of one's ability to breathe: or perhaps seals need some kind of safety back-up in case they forget. Whatever the reasons, in my case, this apnoea was occurring as a result of intermittently putting my face into the very cold water: and believe you me, the continuation of breathing has always been of the utmost importance in my ability to remain both alive and conscious. Both of which states, incidentally, are rather important when finding oneself in cold, and deep, water.

Then, as if all that wasn't sufficient misfortune, I found myself - even in that short time - being introduced to the ravishments of hypothermia. I ask you, as if a chap didn't already have enough on his plate.

Fortunately I wasn't in the water long enough to suffer irreparable damage: and I wasn't aware of a slowing pulse (already occurring as a result of the reflex – why we need two goes at it I don't know, but there we are) or a slowing breathing rate (again, I thought that mine had accompanied my heart and actually stopped). I had, however, noticed an element of fatigue, shivering and pale skin: but that's fair enough, I suppose. The other symptoms didn't manifest themselves until after I got out of the water: more of that shortly.

I managed about a couple of hundred yards of swimming this time, which was about 195 more than the previous time I ventured into the Bay; and I was probably in the water for about ten minutes. Not excessive when compared with the mile and a quarter that separate the Isle of Pelicans from Aquatic Park, or the fifty or so minutes that it would take me to complete the journey; but it was a start, and I felt quite pleased with myself by the time I returned to the extrication point. However, it was then that I was made aware of the other symptoms of hypothermia.

My intention had been to casually approach a gentleman, who was sunning himself on a wooden bench near the water's edge, and ask him if he would kindly help me out of the top half of my rubber attire as I didn't have the strength to pull it over my head. What actually happened, though, was that I staggered across to him, showing little or no control over fine or coarse muscle movements, and said "Cab ooh hippee flob moo sheee … sheee … ah?"

In retrospect, I can quite understand the look of alarm that he proffered in my direction, and the surprising haste with which he terminated his state of repose upon the settle. But to a chap in need of help it did seem a tad discourteous. Fortunately, however, help was at hand - in the shape of Joe, who helped me remove the garment.

He also took the opportunity to outline the effects of hypothermia. Small wonder that I had just given the appearance of a sot with a rubber fetish who had recently had a lobotomy.

My next session was quite a warm day – somewhere in the region of 75 degrees Fahrenheit – and the sun, proudly wearing its new Fedora, was most definitely out and about, shining brightly within a lovely azure blue sky. It's amazing what a dash of sunshine does to a chap's spirits. It's also amazing what putting one's feet into very cold water can do to reverse those uplifting effects.

Anyway, there I was once again, standing on the shore, seeking ways to entice my body back into the Bay. I tried convincing myself that I was in the Bahamas, that the water was a delightful temperature, and that I was simply aching to get going. Worked a treat – for about three seconds: and then it was a question of digging deep into the reserves of Phalarope stoicism.

150

Today's swim had been progressing fairly well (in as much as I hadn't died) when I espied a fellow swimmer to my right. Before I go any further, perhaps I ought to point out that I have the misfortune to suffer (if suffer is the right word) from myopia. In other words, short-sightedness: an inability to clearly focus on things in the distance. Not a huge impediment to one's journey through this vale of tears - especially when compared to some of the afflictions that others have to bear - but when one adds to that the fact I was wearing a pair of swimming goggles that seemed anxious to mist up every few moments it did mean that keen visibility was down to something less than spitting distance: and it was during one of those misty moments that this other swimmer crossed my field of vision.

Hey ho, I thought, as I swam in the general direction of my new companion. It might have been an odd place for a passing 'how do you do', but what the heck.

"Hello," I hailed, in between the rather disconcerting sucking noises I was making as I tried to drag air into my lungs. No response. Perhaps, I further thought, that the brown, leathery swimming-cap I had noticed was hampering his hearing.

I swam closer and called "Hello" again. This time, by the fact that the swimmer had begun to turn around, I reasoned that my interjection had been heard. I also reasoned, when I noticed that the brown leathery material wasn't just confined to the head area - the swimmer seemed to be totally covered in it; apart from the two big brown eyes and some splendid whiskers - that my companion was, in fact, a rather large sea lion. Fortunately for me, a rather friendly one too and, presumably, looking for his friends, whom he must have forgotten were waiting for him at Pier 39.

Then, with a wink of his right eye, the magnificent creature quickly turned and disappeared below the surface. It was well after I had left the water that I paused to muse about what I might have done had the animal been a shark or something equally undesirable. About twenty-five knots I decided.

Another day, and another incursion into the Bay waters. Was it getting any easier? Possibly. I had been told that there would be a period of acclimatisation – or as the citizens of the USA would say 'acclimation'. A wag at the South End Club told me that the first fifteen years were usually the hardest!

While I'm on the subject of cold water, I hadn't realised that Alcatraz was about the only prison in the States that had hot water in the showers – so, it was reasoned, the inmates wouldn't be able to get used to cold water in case they were thinking of making a swim for freedom. Makes sense I suppose.

Speaking of Alcatraz, I took a trip there yesterday. Was I impressed with the island? Up to a point. It certainly looked very much like the images portrayed in Hollywood films: but then, I suppose, it should have. However, I didn't think that the facilities were anywhere near as unpleasant as those to be found in the UK's equivalent – HMP Parkhurst - or quite a few other incarceration establishments for that matter. In case I haven't already mentioned, I have a jolly good chum, Duncan Strewper, who used to be the visiting dentist for Parkhurst.

A frightfully good fellow is Duncan, and always great value at a dinner party; especially if you want to take people's minds off a rather sad foie gras. What tales the man could tell. Riveting they were, and guaranteed to make the hair on the back of your neck perform all sorts of pilo-erective manoeuvres. Not merely a day spent peering into, as he put it, a selection of grubby gobs: indeed not. Duncan used to rub shoulders with all manner of persona non grata: well, at least he sat behind them whilst assailing such as pre-molars with all manner of Jaquettes, pluggers and contra-angle hand-pieces. I shudder when I think about his tales of rubber-dams, reamers and gutta-percha points. Hats off to the fellow though: I'm sure that I couldn't have resisted the temptation - for as long as he did - to apply a Couplands to an area where it wasn't really intended whilst he was treating a particularly unsavoury character.

Fortunately for Duncan, no charges were brought.

Anyway, if only half of what Duncan related was true, I can assure you that, should a comparison be drawn, Alcatraz would come out with several more Egon Ronay stars than a lot of British prisons: what with sea views and individual toilet facilities, and so forth. Having said that though, I don't think 'thrilled' would have been my sentiments had I ever been sent there at anyone's pleasure.

Now where was I? Oh yes, my latest swim. Was it getting enjoyable? Possibly: in a masochistic kind of way. Was I feeling confident about reaching my intended goal? Not exactly, but I was a bit more positive about the outcome than I had been when I embarked upon the undertaking. Was I glad that I had started the venture? Not really, but there I was.

Having used the term 'venture', perhaps I should adopt the mindset of Brutus (that former chum of Julius Caesar) when he spoke of tides in the affairs of men, full seas and taking currents and so forth. Saying that, though, I could hardly be described as being at my height; although I am always in a state of readiness to decline.

So, all things considered, I felt the time had come for a little shortening of the odds against completing the swim. But how?

Would I be able to make the water any warmer? That would certainly help in no small way: but how could that be achieved? I looked through the telephone directories to see if there was a San Francisco Incontinence Society. Maybe if they had keen swimmers amongst their number I could persuade some of them to come along and swim slightly in front of me whilst I made the crossing. That would make the water a bit warmer, but presumably not advisable on health grounds.

A heated swimsuit perhaps. A good idea, I was sure, but would the cable reach that far? Perhaps one that was battery operated? More hopeful; but probably too heavy.

Could I make the distance shorter? That avenue looked as though it was likely to lead me into areas concerning black holes and space-time continuums, and I might not be able to arrange it in time. Or space. Or even understand it. And that concept reminded me of a fellow with whom I once shared a railway carriage. A gentleman who, it must be said, had overly partaken of Bacchanalian delights.

For some reason or another – probably as a result of said gentleman sitting on my lap because he had misjudged the exact location of his hindquarters in relation to any of the vacant seats in the compartment - I found myself engaged in a conversation regarding, paradoxically enough, space. That is, after he produced several minutes of the most profuse apologies to which I had ever been subjected.

I feel I have to describe the overall character of my railway compartment co-occupier in fairly vague terms as I was unable to make any accurate assessment of his persona or lineage: on top of which, he had a very thick Birmingham accent. Not, I hasten to add, that one ought to make any character evaluations on the basis of a fellow's accent, as that should serve only to indicate from which part of our planet's surface he hails. Now I realise that someone with less sensitivity than I would add that they might make an exception in the case of a 'Brummy' accent; but I have always been generously endowed in the diplomacy department.

"Do you ... dooo ... do you know what I think?" my articulatory-challenged companion asked, after he had established that both of his buttocks were safely, and properly, positioned on the seat opposite me.

154

"Indeed I don't. Do tell," I replied, not really meaning it, but fairly certain that he was going to anyway.

"I think – No! ... I *know* how to make space travel faster. I do, you know."

I can remember thinking that living in a world of your own would be a good place to start: and the fellow had obviously found that out for himself. I warily smiled at him. He tapped himself on the side of his nose, and smiled back.

"I don't mean how to make *space* travel faster ... I mean how to make travelling *through* space faster."

"I had a feeling that was what you meant."

"Do you want to know ... how?"

"I am on the very edge of my seat with excitement."

The fellow went to tap himself on the other side of his nose, but missed: three times. He went cross-eyed for a bit, then manhandled the front of his face as he checked to make sure that said proboscis hadn't wandered off without letting him know. As soon as he was convinced that the openings to his maxillary sinuses weren't on display, he continued.

"You shorten the distance between where you are ... and where you're going."

I have to admit that that concept had never occurred to me. Well, apart from when I want to throw balls of paper into a waste-paper basket. I could understand that particular principle: and carry it out. But ...

"And do you know ... how to ... you do ... do that?"

I cautiously shook my head.

"Do you want to know?"

This time I nodded my head, with so much caution that it barely moved.

"You bend the space in between. Ha-ha! Simple! Ha-ha-ha! Ha-ha -"

At that point his eyes glazed over, his eyelids fluttered slightly but did not close, and, keeping his back straight, he toppled, slowly, in a sideways direction. His feet came off the

155

floor for a few seconds, before dropping to floor once again, leaving him lying in a very uncomfortable position along the carriage seat. Discretion, and the fact that the train had arrived at my station, determined that I should leave him where he was.

Well, his idea seemed simple enough. Just bend the space in between. That would certainly make the journey shorter: unless I set off in the wrong direction and ended up swimming along the resultant loop. But I somehow doubted if I would be able to arrange it all before I was due to attempt the swim. I also doubted that my efforts would go unnoticed by other people in the immediate vicinity. I don't know why it is, but there always seems to be something about an impromptu space/time loop that attracts attention.

So, what else was there? I couldn't make the journey shorter, and I couldn't (hygienically) make the water warmer. Hmm. Then, like the proverbial from the blue, it struck me. That is, without all the electrical discharge and burning smells. If I couldn't make the journey shorter or warmer, then what if I made it quicker? Sounded good to me. Quicker would mean having to spend less time in the water, ergo less time in the cold, ergo less time to succumb to the effects of hypothermia. Brilliant!

And to make things easier, would I be able to get the currents, instead of flowing from left to right (and vice versa) as one looks at Alcatraz, to flow in the same direction that I would be swimming? That would be ideal, because I would only have to concentrate on keeping afloat (trapping as much air inside the rubber suit would help enormously) and just let the current do all the work. Ideal, yes, but almost certainly impossible; as not only do time and tide wait for no man, they also have a tendency to completely ignore requests to flow in the preferred direction. What then? Would I be able, in the time I had left, to unravel the mystery that is Quantum Entanglement? Not very likely; but another zap to the old frontal lobes brought the solution. Flippers - or as they prefer to call them in California, fins. That was it! Fins: and, presumably, the bigger the better.

After a brisk hot shower, I was back on the Powell-Hyde cable-car, heading for the turn-around near Market Street, and then on to Copeland's. A ten-minute rummage around one of the lower shelves in the swimming goods area found a pair of rather fetching blue and black U.S. Divers Aqua-Lung flippers: just the job. Another five minutes found some very strange-looking webbed gloves as well: even better.

A slight taste of caution then disseminated within in my mouth as images of my old physics teacher suddenly floated before my eyes: big flippers and big gloves would need big efforts to move them through the water. Another rummage through the memory bank found Newton's 'Principia', and a First Law that states 'Every body (and that, I was certain, was going to include me) continues in its state of rest unless it is compelled to change that state by forces impressed on it'.

Well, being a fairly languid sort of chap, I am always in favour of continuing in any state of rest. But being of fairly erudite inclinations as well (brought about, let it be known, by a mixture of favourable genetics and a private education), I soon realised that a continuing state of rest wasn't going to do much in the way of propelling me across the stretch of water in question. Forward movement was going to involve, if I wanted the required equal and opposite reaction, some sort of initial action. Unfortunate, but there didn't seem to be any way round it: some brand of increased physical activity on my part was still going to be called for.

And so, proudly, I strode to the checkout with my prospective purchases, trying to deal with the myriad of 'you're a bit of a cheat' type thoughts that seemed over-keen to foist themselves into those areas of my grey matter that are designed to deal with issues of conscience. I finally managed to assuage them by pointing out that a cheat is always more desirable at a dinner table than a shrivelled blue cadaver: both from appearance, and the variety of tales with which they might regale the other guests.

My mental wrestling was then interrupted by the young lady stationed at the point of imbursement.

"I don't have a bag big enough to put your items in, sir," she said, looking obsequiously disappointed.

"Worry ye not," I replied, anxious to try out a bit of the famous Phalarope irony. "I shall wear them home."

The look of astonishment on the young lady's face told me that she, like a good number of her compatriots, was suffering from that oft discussed irony deficiency. And anyway, as if my suggestion should have caused concern – I had seen many people on the BART system who had been attired in apparel of far greater unsuitability. I decided, rather than try to explain my levity, to graciously pay and depart.

On the morning of my next dip in the Bay, I awoke with genuine feelings of excitement. Flippers and webbed gloves. Hooray! And the sun was shining as well. Mind you, that last statement was almost unnecessary as it shone most days. However, it sounds cheery, so in it goes.

Perhaps, in order to temper any excessive anticipation amongst the readers, I ought to mention that I had only worn flippers on one previous occasion; and that was as a ten-year old in the swimming pool at my prep school. Perhaps, also at this juncture, I ought to point out that I should have considered the differences between the physical effort required - whilst wearing said flippers - to gain access to calm water by way of poolside tiles and that needed to gain access to wave-infested water by means of a sloping sandy beach. They are, as I was soon to discover, numerous and paramount.

In the poolside instance, one is simply required to strap the aforementioned accessories to one's feet, and then, either by lying down and rolling towards the wet area or jumping with an accompanying yell (Banzai or Geronimo usually worked best for me) one is able to bring together all the ingredients required for the exercise. But this system was not going to work in the second instance.

Firstly, because lying down and rolling across a beach towards the wet stuff does little else but fill one's facial cavities with an extraordinary amount of sand and, unless you have a reliable sense of direction, it can often leave you further away from the water than you were at the beginning.

Secondly, because jumping into the air (with or without the accompanying yell) will only land you in about twelve inches of water, and this has a tendency to cause a very painful jarring of the back when you make contact with the floor. That situation could, I should imagine, be avoided if, by an extraordinary coincidence, you happen to be a gifted long-jumper who normally trains wearing flippers.

So, after several minutes of deliberation, I decided to execute the procedure by simply walking down the slope and into the water. Oh, what a foolish man I was. To begin with, walking in a forward direction across wet sand in flippers is nigh on impossible; no matter how hard I concentrated, I was unable to prevent the forward edge of the flippers from digging into the sand: and this had three effects. One, that I then had to lift each foot about eighteen inches off the ground with each step I took; two, that lifting the flippers off the sand served merely to flick several cupfuls of the stuff into my eyes; and three, the elderly gentleman who had, hitherto, been enjoying a quiet rest in the sun, entered a near paroxysmal state of coughing brought on by an inability to laugh with great gusto whilst swallowing a mouthful of hot coffee.

I decided, upon nearing the water and its attendant swell, that it might be a good idea if I grabbed hold of the edge of the wooden pier that ran alongside me. This, I have to admit, greatly increased my firmness of foot; but, coupled with the fact that I was sporting a pair of bright yellow webbed gloves, it also greatly decreased my already rapidly dwindling decorum.

However, dignity and deportment aside, I eventually reached a sufficient depth to enable me to try out my new acquisitions: and what a difference they made! With less than a debilitating increase in effort, and probably a good deal more élan, I was able to cut a swathe through the water that would have done credit to Mark Spitz. The euphoria that this produced lasted well up to the time that, because of the still penetrating cold, I decided to vacate the brine: and that was when I fell foul of two unforeseen outcomes of my performance-enhancing additions.

The first was that I had taken the precaution – as an adjunct to the existing, and perfectly adequate, strapping that enabled the flippers to remain attached to my feet – of using some twine to tie the flippers to my ankles. That, of itself, should have caused no anxiety; but when I had tied the knots, my fingers had been relatively responsive to the instructions they had received from the posterior part of my frontal lobes. On leaving the water, however, my fingers seemed to be under the control of an inhabitant of the planet 'Blotto' who had been over-imbibing liquids that had, at one time or another, been exposed to sugar and yeast.

The second drawback, if the first was not sufficient cause for irritation, was that I found – as a result of moving through the water a little faster than my previous experience – that the waist-band of my rubber trousers had not been able to maintain its erstwhile tight grip on my waist; and this had caused the trousers to fill up with water.

"So what?" I hear you ask.

Well, let me tell you 'so what'.

The rubber was waterproof and, as I may have mentioned, gathered in tightly at the ankle region. Beginning to get the picture? The result was that I looked like a native from central Africa who had recently been infected with the parasite Filaria and subsequently contracted elephantiasis. Not an attractive sight at the best of times; but when said unfortunate is then seen waving

160

large yellow hands, hopping around on large blue feet, before landing on his back and waggling said blue feet in the air whilst giving the appearance of a collapsing bladder, the overall effect is sufficient to make one look for a dark hole, crawl into it, and wait until approached by a tall gentleman, dressed in black, who happens to be carrying a large scythe.

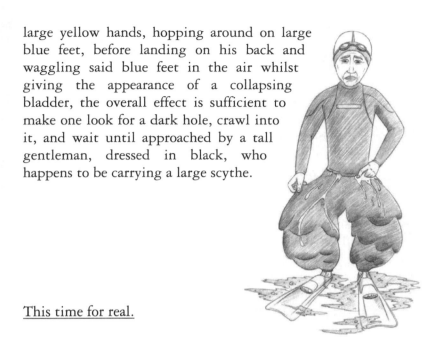

This time for real.

Anyway, despite numerous incantations to the gods of procrastination, the day of the swim finally arrived. I had posted some inquisitive e-mails to members of both the South End and the Dolphin clubs to ask if anybody might care to accompany me on my venture – both in the hope of safety in case hypothermia should creep up on me, and, in a slightly parsimonious vein, to possibly share the cost of the speed-boat that I was hiring for the purpose. I received three replies.

The first advised me to take a pen so that I could send them a postcard from Maui (something to do with the prevailing currents at the intended time of my undertaking); the second pointed out that a swimmer had more chance of being spotted when on his own than in a group; the third, slightly less than encouraging, advised me to forget the whole thing and take up macramé instead.

The last piece of advice, although well meant I'm sure, did little to spur me on. The first suggestion saw to it that I checked the tide times and, as a result, I brought the swim forward by a couple of hours.

And so, at nine-thirty on the second Friday of October, I found myself sitting in the back of a very nice, white, rigid-hull, Zodiac inflatable and speeding out towards the island of Alcatraz. There was little wind, it was sunny, and the air temperature was in the high sixties. All was well; or at least it would have been if I had been able to sit back and enjoy it.

There was, I have to admit, a slight feeling of the condemned man about me. Not because I was expecting to die, or even lose a limb to a passing shark, but mainly because, for me at least, this was, to put it mildly, a bit of a step outside my normal sphere of activity: and, not to put it mildly, a gigantic leap away from my comfort zone. If you had asked me a year ago – or even five weeks earlier – if there was a possibility that I might be trying to swim from Alcatraz back to the San Francisco, I would have suggested that you booked an appointment to see a phrenologist as soon as possible.

But there I was, about to get into the cold waters of San Francisco Bay, and attempt to do just that. Well, not *just* that: I was also in the process of trying to wrap myself up in several layers of tin foil.

"What!" I hear you cry.

Let me explain. I hit upon the idea, whilst watching a television advertisement to do with correct food preparation, that wrapping a layer of heat-reflective foil around my midriff, and thighs, and forearms, might go some way to staving off the moment when the surrounding dearth of degrees Fahrenheit would make their absence felt upon my encompassing epithelium. So, whilst skimming over the water in the boat, I was struggling, with the aid of several strips of duct-tape and the right hand of the man who was in charge of the Zodiac, to fix said tin foil to my torso and limbs.

162

This procedure would not have been particularly easy in the comfort of my own living-room, but whilst bouncing across the tops of small waves, and having to prevent my companion from laughing himself out of the boat, it became a matter of no small difficulty. However, after a number of attempts, the job was completed and my black rubber suit was then pulled into place.

By that time, I might add, I was rather hot and rather bothered, and felt in a unique position to empathise with oven-ready turkeys: and fairly secure in the knowledge that should I drift far off course, the coastguard would have no difficulty in picking me up on his radar. I was only surprised that I wasn't able to receive local radio stations at the same time.

Ten minutes later, and with the Zodiac as near Alcatraz as the driver could take it without attracting the displeasure of the local rangers, I slipped over the side; and with a cheery wave, I began to strike out for Aquatic Park.

I don't know if any of you have ever swum in open waters, but I found it to be a very strange experience. Strange, because I wanted to enjoy what I was doing, but at the same time I wanted to get it over with as soon as possible. Strange, because I felt isolated from reality, and yet acutely aware of what might be swimming below me. Strange, because when I had previously gone swimming it was within the cluttered confines of a local swimming baths: but now, whenever I looked up, I could see the Golden Gate Bridge and the Transamerica Pyramid.

Speaking of contrasts and local swimming baths, why is it that whenever I go swimming – at times that I think it should be fairly quiet – there is always some idiot there who feels compelled to swim like a 'wind-up' doll (arms thrashing about in the whirling motion more often associated with a demented banshee), and another who doesn't understand what the concept of 'swimming in lanes' means. People like that should be summarily harpooned and immediately removed from the pool.

But will the poolside attendants attend to these miscreants? The short answer is 'No'. They are quite happy to

163

parade up and down the side of the pool – or even spend time in an elevated sitting position – blowing whistles and telling people not to jump on top of others; but they seem loath to deal with inconsiderate swimming practices. Mind you, I don't suppose these people have been hired because they can write a thesis on utilitarianism.

Speaking of vacuous members of society, I have sometimes had occasion – actually, I think 'been given' the occasion might be more accurate; although 'forced on the point of death if I didn't' might be even closer - to take my niece swimming (when the lass was about six years old as I recall). On one such, I was accompanying her as she splashed her way from the shallow to the deep end. We were about two-thirds of the way along, when I heard an overly shrill whistle, followed by a rather irritating voice that emanated from a somewhat pimply girl, who informed me my niece wasn't allowed down the deep end until she could swim two lengths of the pool.

Until that moment I hadn't considered the likelihood of looking incredulous whilst treading water and, as it so happened, simultaneously considering whether people with unpleasant skin should be allowed anywhere near public baths: but it turned out to be perfectly possible.

"What?" I recall asking, shaking my head to clear any residual water from my external auditory meatuses, in case I had misheard.

"I said she can't go dahn the deep-end unless she can swim two lenfs."

"What?" I repeated: only this time I employed a tone that should have left the intended recipient of my remark in no doubt I had the impression that should she ever decide to indulge in a course of trepanation, she had best be careful to ensure that any nearby items of furniture were nailed down in case they got sucked into the vacuum that clearly existed within the confines of her cranium.

"I said she can't go dahn the deep-end unless she can swim two lenfs."

"My dear girl, I shall give you the benefit of the doubt and assume that you are intentionally indulging in a spot of merry absurdity. Albert Camus would have been delighted, I'm sure. So, for that moment of wit, I thank you: and now we must be on our way."

"Eh?"

"Quite."

My niece and I continued with our swim.

"Oi! I said you can't do that."

"I know you did. And I'm not going to have a semantic discussion about whether *can't* or *mustn't* should have been the word of choice, but I will go so far as to point out – to which I have already made reference – the absurdity of your remark."

"Wot?"

"My dear girl, is there anyone employed within a quarter of a mile of our present whereabouts who might have more understanding of the English language than you seem to possess?"

"Uh?"

Oh dear, I thought, as images of brick walls and banging heads against same began to float before my eyes. Then, with a sharpness that might, by some, have been considered to sound less than charitable, I told the young attendant that perhaps - before she left me in no doubt that she ought not to have played hookey quite as often as she did whilst her class-mates, presumably, were receiving the, albeit meagre, benefits of whatever education was being provided by the local authorities - she ought to go and seek out someone who might have had occasion to look inside the Concise Oxford from time to time.

With the image of her leaping up and down whilst furiously waving her arms about and screaming several local council by-law regulations, my niece and I resumed our course. We successfully reached the far end of the pool, and were about halfway through the return leg when our attention was once more requested: this time by a short man (no surprise there then), whose attempts to use stentorian tones would have received very odd looks from most RSMs. There is something signally unappealing about a loud voice that has a pronounced 'whiney' timbre permeating every syllable.

"Yes?" I politely enquired, not wishing to cause his already bulging eyes to pop out altogether. Especially not into the water, as their colouring would make them quite difficult to pick out from the tiled flooring. Although, upon reflection, the red capillaries that quivered through his conjunctivae might have expedited that task.

"Are you the guy that was rude to a member of my staff?"

"By 'member of staff', do you mean the somewhat feeble-minded individual with whom I had occasion to speak earlier?"

"Er ... yeah."

"And, by 'rude', are you referring to the fact that I took the trouble to bring to *her* attention the ludicrousness of the point that she was striving to bring to *my* attention?"

"Listen mate, I don't know what you're talking about, but ... but anyway, that kid with you shouldn't be there. Not there. Not until she's done two lengths."

"Is that so?"

"Yeah."

"Then I think that I ought to take this opportunity to make two observations. Both of which you might like to consign to your memory banks for future reference. Firstly, I am not your mate. And secondly, how is this 'kid' – as you put it - supposed to swim two lengths if she is not allowed down the deep end?" I now had images of Joseph Heller in my mind's eye. "Hmm?"

"She ... that is ... if ... she could ..."

"Well ...?"

"Has she done it?"

"What?"

"The two lengths?"

166

"Very nearly. In fact she would have completed the task about ten minutes ago if we hadn't been interrupted. Twice."

"Right. Okay then. Just don't let it happen again. Right."

With that, the somewhat deflated fellow scurried from our sight, and my niece and I were able to complete our goal. Such incidents do make me wonder why it is that so many stupid – or should I say 'intellectually challenged'? No, I think I prefer 'stupid' – people seem so anxious to display their cerebral shortcomings. Maybe there is a clue in the question. Now, where was I? Oh yes, swimming from Alcatraz.

People have since asked me if I was concerned about the thought of what might be swimming below me, or about the depth of water itself. To the latter I would say 'no', as I have always been perfectly capable of drowning in water that was six inches deeper than the distance from my mouth to my feet, never mind one hundred feet or more. To the former, I would say that I tried not to let my mind drift in that direction and concentrated, instead, on counting thirty strokes so that I might raise my head at regular intervals in order to check that I was still heading towards my intended destination.

Fishes have never been a great favourite of mine: unless separated from me by a pane of glass or a layer of batter. I know that they have a longer attention span and a greater memory than is commonly thought, and I am the first to admit that I wouldn't recognise a Black Widow Tetra if it swam up my trouser leg; but there is something about them that seems quite alien. Perhaps it's the shape of their heads, or perhaps the way they feel when you touch them. As for the way their eyes always seem to follow me whenever I walk past the display counter of a fishmonger ... Having said that, as I may have mentioned previously, I do have a pond of the things in my garden.

I remember once deciding to clear out said fishpond. Fair enough, I thought, one or two of them were, perhaps, a bit on the large side; but there was no real possibility of me losing a body part.

Perhaps I should start by explaining why the pond needed cleaning in the first place. The water had become so thick with plants and detritus that the only time I ever saw the fishes was when they came to the surface to either grab a bite to eat or gulp in some much needed oxygen. Although I say 'saw the fishes', what I really mean is that I was able to see their mouths: and nothing else.

Intent on first removing the fishes, I used a pump to drain out as much water as I felt it could handle before succumbing to the damaging effects of pure silt. Next, with most of the water out the way, the plan was to scoop up the fishes with one of those net-on-a-stick things, one by one as the lower level of water made them easier to see, and transfer them to a child's paddling pool that I had previously placed nearby and filled with fresh water

This continued according to plan until I had eventually placed them all in the clear water. I have to say, that catching them wasn't as easy as picking apples out of a barrel. Those blighters did all they could to avoid capture; but the superior intellect prevailed and, after about an hour and a half, I had them all ten of them in the paddling pool.

Although, to be perfectly honest, it did seem as if the fishes had been playing some kind of a game with me. They would lead me a merry dance for several minutes and then, as if tiring of their new found source of amusement, they would swim into the net, give me a look that spoke volumes about how highly they regarded my net-handling abilities, and casually swim out again as I placed them in the clear water.

But I was able to have the last laugh: or so I thought at the time. Once in the fresh water, having jauntily waggled their way out of the net, the fishes stopped in their tracks. I was initially at a loss to explain this, but then realised, by careful observation, that the fishes, after years of living in what essentially amounted to a rather thick pea soup, were now able to see more than a couple of inches in front of them and were, almost certainly, suffering from agoraphobia: and possibly oxygen poisoning as well. But as I was unlikely, unable and, certainly, unwilling to perform an autopsy on any of them, I couldn't confirm that. So reasoned observation it had to remain.

Agoraphobic fishes indeed! Thinking about it, I'm rather surprised that some enterprising individuals haven't set up in business as fish counsellors: maybe they already have. I understand that you can get your Labrador psychoanalysed – for a handsome fee, of course - presumably to discover if coming from a broken litter was the reason the animal was chewing your furniture. A fool and his money, eh. Anyway, my fishes soon came to terms with being able to see each other and, presumably, breathe through clean water.

Having guessed that they were unlikely to suffer any lasting mental trauma, my wave of concern soon dissipated on the shoreline of harmony and I returned my attention back to the leguminous quagmire that remained. The pump was quite obviously struggling to deal with the sludge, so I decided to climb in and shift the rest with the aid of a large bucket.

Good thinking, I thought, as I lowered the level further. Who says that those years of private education were a waste of – "Good grief," I suddenly exclaimed, when my gaze fell upon what I perceived to be a Wellington boot.

"How the devil did that get there?" I further articulated, as I trudged through the remaining morass to remove the offending article.

My next exclamation began "What the - ", but I feel, for the sake of propriety, I should omit the rest of the quote. Suffice it to say, the large black, rubber-looking object upon which my gaze had fallen was not, in fact, a galosher, but a rather belligerent, old – and, by now, thoroughly discombobulated – tench, who has since answered to the name of Dan.

Unfortunately for me, and, I suspect, in some small way for Dan as well, I did not realise the difference until I had grasped hold of what I thought was the 'open' end of said Wellington, only to find it was the featheredge of a 'soon to be wildly flapping' Caudal fin.

I'm not sure who jumped the highest. I know that Dan probably gave it his all, but as I had a certain height advantage to begin with, I feel, on further contemplation, that the honours almost certainly went in my direction. But you will all be pleased to know that the pool was cleaned, refilled and all the fishes made a satisfactory return; and neither Dan nor I show any signs of having suffered at all as a result of our experience.

So there I was, back in the Bay, counting out the strokes and raising my head from time to time, whilst trying to ignore the cold that was slowly, and inexorably, finding its way through my tin-foil and rubber attire. I know that the chap in charge of the Zodiac was shouting words of encouragement in my direction – at least that was what he told me afterwards – but, thanks to the glutinous blue wax I had shoved in my ears (to prevent ingress of the cold water which, I had been reliably informed, would play havoc with the movement of the otoliths within my semi-circular canals, and thus cause extreme motion sickness), I was unable to distinguish other than what seemed like a gentle braying on his part. I gave the fellow a friendly wave of acknowledgement, nevertheless, and continued with my odyssey.

It was about three-quarters of the way across that the currents and my rapidly diminishing awareness of direction - and equally rapidly diminishing concern about what I was doing - combined to ensure that I started to veer (if one is capable of veering at a speed of one mile an hour) in more of a westward direction than I had intended.

My companion was now yelling at me with as much verve as he could rally but, thanks to the aforementioned ear-occupiers (and covering swim-cap), I was unable to hear what he was saying: and, as I have already intimated, I was pretty much past caring. The net result was that I missed the entrance to Aquatic Park by some way and ended up coming ashore at a place known as East Harbour.

Not that I really minded. I was just elated to have completed the swim and, after a wave from me of confirmation to show that all was well, my companion signalled his congratulations before returning to somewhere called Sausalito.

My euphoria was soon tempered by the realisation that I was going to have to walk the half-mile or so back to the South End Club ... in my black rubber and tin-foil outfit ... and, as my fingers were nowhere near being able to respond to my commands, with my flippers still firmly tied in place. My initial fear of impending embarrassment was soon placated by the realisation that such a sight was not uncommon, nor unexpected, in San Francisco.

As I recall, the only interest I aroused came from a small group of Japanese tourists, upon the walls of whose rooms, I am quite sure, must now hang framed photographs of my contribution to the never-ending eccentricity of the erstwhile Yerba Buena. Even the chap who opened the door of the club to me didn't bat an eyelid.

<u>Hitchcock and Gabriella</u>.

I went to see three films while I was a guest of San
Francisco; the first of which was an upgraded version of Lawrence
of Arabia. The same cast (same film really), but reputed to have
been digitally re-mastered - and before you ask, no I don't know
what that means — with the addition of several scenes that had
been cut from the original rendering. I believe that one of them
was the 'long shot' when Omar Shariff makes his first appearance:
can't be sure though.

Anyway, it was being shown at a cinema known as the
Castro Theatre. A splendid place - designed (for the aficionados in
such matters) in Spanish Baroque by a chap named Timothy
Plueger - that has high, ornate balconies and wall-mounted busts
of heroic figures: and, rather a plus point from my perspective,
there was a pre-screen playing of a 'mighty' Wurlitzer-type organ.
Splendid stuff, with, appropriately enough, several tunes from
'The White Horse Inn' and 'The Desert Song'. It was with great
personal discipline that I refrained from joining in with my
rendition of 'One Alone'.

Actually, to be perfectly honest, it didn't take that much
discipline as I wanted to watch the film; and being escorted from
the premises for upsetting the people within earshot wasn't really
going to achieve that end. Also, I think the fruit stains on my
clothes would have taken an age to wash out: and it may well not
have stopped at fruit.

Have you seen the size of the cartons that are provided for
popcorn? Buckets might be a better description. They must hold
the best part of a hundredweight of the stuff: and the cola
containers weren't much smaller either.

But back to the theatre: and its organ. There is something
about organ playing that always stirs my blood: rather like brass
bands. The rest of the audience was enjoying it as well; especially
when the excerpts that I recognised came to end and, as a finale,

172

the organist began thumping out the Judy Garland hit 'San Francisco'. Those assembled gleefully, and very loudly, clapped and sang along. This, I was later to discover, is a regular event, and both the song and Miss Garland occupy a special place with the usual audience that attends that particular venue.

The Castro Theatre is in - unsurprisingly - the Castro district of the City. And, before you ask, no I didn't know that Miss Garland is something of (as they put it) a Gay Icon, or (at the time) that the Castro is an area heavily frequented by persons whose sexual inclinations are totally dissimilar to my own. But I did notice that the cinema was packed with said persons.

"So what?" I can hear.

Well, once again, I'll tell you 'so what'. Lawrence of Arabia – or T.E Lawrence as he was sometimes known (Thomas to his friends): although he later called himself Ross, and then finally changed his name (by deed poll) to T.E. Shaw – was a man about whose 'sexuality' much has been speculated. I am not going to point fingers, or make deprecating comments, but much of the audience in the cinema had not only clearly formed their own opinion on the subject, but they also felt obliged to vocally express it, with every opportunity that arose, at any physical gesture or spoken word in the film that could have been misinterpreted.

A raised eye-brow here, a purse of the lips there, even a delicate hand motion somewhere else, brought with it an eruption of bawdy laughter from most quarters of the auditorium. I suppose we had a similar arrangement back in the UK with the 'Round the Horn' radio show, if you can recall, involving lawyers and their criminal practices.

On top of all this innuendo-based ribaldry, there was a man – not many seats from my own – who felt obliged to let the rest of the patrons deduce that he was extremely well-versed in matters pertaining to Turkish-Arab relations during the First World War (and thereabouts) by laughing out aloud (on his own) whenever a political aspect of the period was alluded to: especially

173

those that may not have shown the British input to the proceedings in a particularly favourable light. Sadly, as the film progressed, it seemed that his routine was beginning to catch on somewhat.

I have to say that I was beginning to feel my hackles rising, and was within a jibe or two of going over and straightening out the most vociferous proclaimer of Anglophobic statements when I noticed - and I have to add, lest I seem intent on denigrating our American cousins – that most of them did take the trouble to laugh at the less than flattering contributions which the Americans were making to the whole debacle.

It was also quite interesting to watch a film that had been made without the interference of the 'USA is Great' brigade that hangs around Hollywood these days, or had been subjected to the ravages of politically correct censors. That kind of 'thought police' action really does scare me.

But speaking of 'Hollywoodizing' history, I recently read about one of their latest releases – one based on the escapes from Colditz during the Second World War. It was all about how American POWs managed - brilliantly and daringly - to escape from the prison castle. Eh? To my knowledge, not one single American whatsoever took part in an escape attempt; and, in fact, no American officer was even present when the attempts were made. Not one!

Then we had the film that recounted how, during the same war, the Americans captured an 'Enigma' machine. Excuse me? I have always been under the impression that the British already had 'Enigma' before America joined the war. I also understood that members of the Polish resistance were rather prominently involved; and that names like Turing, Hinsley and Welchman, along with HMS Bulldog and Petard, ought to have been given quite a lot of the credit. However, perhaps the names of Colin Grazier, Tony Fasson and Tommy Brown and their acts of heroism in the sinking U-559 should get the greatest accolade of all.

Did Hollywood see fit to commend any of the above? Of course not.

"The films," bleat the producers, "are only dramas."

Oh really? I wonder what the reaction would be if we (the British) made some films that showed how we (the British) won the American War of Independence? Or that the first man who walked on the moon came from Chipping Sodbury and was called Nigel? I rather think that, even if we labelled them as being merely 'dramas', there would be a bit of a stink raised. One rule for one, another for another: as usual! I'm not going to get started on the travesties that were perpetrated in the films 'Titanic' and 'Mutiny on the Bounty': even though I would really like to.

But, regardless of all that, I enjoyed the film: and, so it seemed, did just about everyone else in the cinema.

My second film was, by way of an invitation, to a special showing of Alfred Hitchcock's 'Rear Window', at a private library. Someone from the magazine had been very kind and lent me their library card for a couple of weeks, which allowed me access to said library - situated at the end of Post Street – because he thought that I might get an insight into another facet of City life: how right he was.

What a collection of people I found there. I am not usually a frequenter of libraries - either public or private - so I am not really in a position to comment on whether or not such a variety is usually to be found in those temples to tomes; so I shall refrain from passing judgement and just mention a few of those I saw on the days I spent browsing through the shelves.

There was a gentleman who had obviously based his appearance on the professor from the Tin-Tin stories; another who had not slept (or shaved) for several days and felt the need to catch up on his slumber would be best achieved in one of the arm-chairs; a woman who thought that (whilst using one of the internet stations available) coughing every thirty seconds would help her (and all the other library users) to concentrate; and (possibly my favourite) the elderly man who made changing a duvet cover look simple when compared to the trouble that he was having in folding his newspaper.

Great fun to watch, I have to say.

But I digress: the Hitchcock film. I was shown to a small room that had a white screen hanging from the ceiling, and several rows of hard-backed chairs facing towards it. I graciously accepted the glass of red wine that was offered and went and sat down on one of the vacant chairs.

Shortly afterwards, a rather pompous-looking gentleman, with shoulder-length (unnaturally wavy) hair, a very sharp suit and the practically (for, in my opinion, low-level lecturers) mandatory bow-tie, came and stood in front of a lectern that had been positioned in a corner of the room.

"Good evening, ladies and gentlemen," he began.

So far, so good, I reflected.

"And may I welcome you all to this evening's movie and discussion."

Discussion? Nobody said anything about a discussion.

"My name is Schlomo Fossilburger."

Oh, that's just perfect, I thought, as I struggled to prevent my mouthful of wine from going anywhere other than towards my stomach.

"We have chosen, as our paradigm of clandestine implications ..." *Eh?* "... the much-acclaimed 'Rear Window'. Although 'Rear Window' masquerades – quite successfully – as a piece of light entertainment, it is an enormously complex movie." *Double Eh?* "Adapted from Cornell Woolrich's short story – 'It had to be murder' - this is a movie in which Hitchcock – the consummate virtuoso – was in full command of his technique. Yet technique alone ... "

It was about then that I began to wonder if I was in the right place. My ticket read, very clearly, that I had been invited to watch 'Rear Window'. It did not mention anything about a lengthy pre-amble given by a man who, quite obviously, enjoyed the sound of his own voice and appeared to feel obligated to inflict it upon a room full of undeserving strangers. My concentration returned for a moment: the gentleman was still talking.

" ... glimpses of an awareness that was at odds with the icon-like stature which Hitchcock had created for himself. That, incidentally, I am sure you will agree, of the master of a cinematic MO which mocks his ..."

I could feel my eyelids closing. I don't know about you, but when I go to see a film it is usually because I want to watch, and enjoy, the film. Not because I want to dissect it; and then, with a bunch of (as yet to be confirmed) similarly-minded individuals, pore over the results of their deliberations. No; I just want to watch the film, laugh a little, feel sad; maybe even get a bit scared. But mainly to enjoy it. A simple enough approach, I would have thought.

" ... is often labelled a misanthrope, and even a misogynist, there is evidence of a sympathy – maybe even empathy – for the loneliness that leads to voyeurism. But I also feel that there is a lot to be said for the incredible location of the movie, which is ..."

Zzzzzzzzzzzzzzzz

" ... and blunt humour. Now, are there any questions?"

Silence prevailed for a moment. Rather like the silence when an irritating fly has left the room. I slowly opened my eyes.

"Yes sir. You at the back."

I looked to my right to see at whom the attention was being directed. It was a rather dishevelled old man, with grey, untidy hair, a jacket that looked as though he regularly slept in it, and a pair of glasses with a black frame and lenses that looked thick enough to take my weight. He slowly got to his feet.

"Is ..." he falteringly spoke. "Is ... er ..."

"Yes ..."

"Is ... er ... is Jimmy Stooert in it?"

I very nearly stood up and applauded the question; but managed to control my instincts to acknowledge sublime satire when I realised that the old man wasn't trying to make a point: he genuinely wanted to know if Jimmy Stewart was in the film.

"Ahm ... yes," came the almost indignant reply.

"Good. I like ... Jimmy Stooert."

"Great. Okay then ... let's roll the movie."

So roll it, they did: and I enjoyed the film. I won't say that I raved about it, or would describe it as one of my all-time favourites: I enjoyed it. As simple as that. And having watched it all the way through, that is when, under normal circumstances, I would have picked up my hat and coat, and quietly left the cinema: but tonight was not a normal circumstance.

No sooner had the film ended and the lights gone up again, than the resident cinematography expert popped up once more and, after a few words of thanks for the projectionist, he invited another expert to join him at the lectern and deliver a few words.

Oh good, I thought in a less than charitable vein of sarcasm, and wondered if there was any way in which I could dematerialise. Or, perhaps in a paroxysmal fit of coughing, find a plausible reason for facilitating my egress.

"Okay then," began the new addition to the edification committee, "let's discuss what we have just watched. Now, did everyone feel the same sentiment that I found to be prevalent throughout the entire movie?" *Eh?* "Were we all drawn into the story?" *Wasn't that the whole point?* "Did we all feel the same empathy towards the characters?" *I've no idea. Unless some of the other men here found Grace Kelly as attractive as I did. Although, knowing the likely cross-section, maybe Jimmy 'Stooert' was higher up the list.* "Would anybody like to make a comment?"

I then sat and listened as three, might have been four, people asked questions that, rather than elicit an answer from the MC, seemed more intended as a vehicle for showing off their extensive knowledge of trivia concerning Hitchcock films. Whatever it is that possesses people and makes them spend their time memorising minutiae concerning films, football teams or train timetables I shall never know: or understand. Perhaps they just have an inbuilt flair for such matters and have no other avenue in which to display their talents. For my own part, I have trouble remembering where I left my car keys. But then came another question.

"Was the movie," asked a lady from the row behind mine, "a means by which we were meant to explore our innermost feelings on voyeurism?"

I have to be honest here, and say that my opinion of whatever question the aforementioned lady might have asked would have been on the glowing side of good: even if I didn't have a clue what she meant. And before anybody asks if W. Phalarope Esq. is the type of fellow who feels his knees go a bit wobbly when confronted with a member of the opposite sex whose features could accurately be described as stunning, I shall hold up my hand and plead in the affirmative. Yes, indeed. Show me a Helen and I'll show you a very good impersonation of an Aurelia Aurita.

The lady was gorgeous; and I mean gorgeous with a capital 'Guh'. Auburn hair – maybe a bit more red than auburn, but delightful nonetheless – that fell loosely across her shoulders, green eyes that sparkled like wet emeralds in early morning sunshine, and lips that had been designed in such a way that left me in no doubt that God was very much in favour of osculation. And, despite being an American, she spoke eloquently.

Now, before all those 'never judge a book by its cover' activists leap to their feet and screech apophthegms at me about how I should never judge a book by its cover, I shall recount the lesson I learned when – many moons ago – I was waiting to pay for some items at a supermarket, and my gaze happened upon a young lady in the queue at the adjacent checkout. I should perhaps mention that in the attractiveness department I have often been described as passable: provided, as my mother would delight in adding, that I am seen at dusk with a strong light behind me. But being the eternal optimist that I am, I hurriedly left my queue and dashed over to join hers; in the slight, but almost certainly vain, hope of engaging her in conversation and possibly, by impressing her, I might even (with a following wind, that is) venture to ask if she might feel an inclination to adjourn to a location more conducive to future concord. Without, that is, appearing in any way pompous.

I can recall standing astern of the young Aphrodite, racking my grey matter as to the best method of initiating a dialogue, when Eros himself, as if realising my quandary, reached into his quiver and sent forth an arrow. Only instead of catching the young lady around the fourth or fifth intercostal space on the left-hand side, the arrow must have hit her in the back of the hand; and the bag of sugar she was about to place on the conveyor

180

belt shot into the air and landed, with a 'splumf', all over my shoes.

Being the sort of fellow who recognises a heaven-sent opportunity when it happens along, I gave as nonchalant a shake of the noggin as I could, and said that she wasn't to concern herself as leather was made to easily withstand a couple of pounds of Tate & Lyle's finest. I felt sure the way had been paved for a fruitful liaison.

"Oh fanks mate," she then effused all over me. "No, I dunno wot 'appened. That bleedin' packet just slipped and ... 'ere, did you say levver? That's a bit posh, innit?"

If the Tannoy hadn't chosen that exact moment to remind customers about a particular item being on special offer for a limited period only, you would have clearly heard the Phalarope jaw hitting the ground.

"Quite," I managed, as soon as I had relocated both of my mandibular condyles within their respective fossae. Fortunately, further need to converse was obviated when the young lady began to argue with the lank-haired youth at the checkout about the expiry dates on several coupons that she had handed to him.

I discreetly slipped away and spent the next twenty minutes hiding in the cold meat section.

Anyway, before I digress further, back to the dazzling lady. "Was the movie a means by which we were meant to explore our innermost feelings on voyeurism?" she had asked.

What an incisive question, I thought; and it was asked with a voice that must have been on loan from Aglaophonus. Had she been yelling at me from Anthemoessa, I would have, quite gladly, steered my vessel straight for the rocks. Forget the precautions of Jason and Odysseus: I would have wanted to let those dulcet tones, with their tender oscillations, tap gently upon my tympanic membranes: to feel the ecstasy as my Malleus, Incus and Stapes passed the vibration on to my fenestra ovalis: to savour the delights – calm down William, old thing. But what a way to go!

181

Up until that point I didn't even know that I had innermost feelings about voyeurism: or outermost ones, for that matter. But now I wanted to do more than explore the possibilities. I wanted to get a comfortable deckchair, a blanket, a pair of binoculars, and observe every aspect on offer.

How foolish I had been to think that 'Rear Window' was just a story told on celluloid. Tsk! This lady – have I mentioned how lovely she was? – with just one sentence made me aware of how much more the film had to offer. Of course Hitchcock used this film to offer glimpses of a sensibility at odds with the image that Hitchcock created for himself. Of course it enabled me to develop empathy for the women in it. Of course it exquisitely balanced an interest in the main plot with a developing concern about the many – and varied, I might add – subplots. As for the voyeuristic tendencies that a prolonged spell of ennui can produce … Well, my mind was overcome with a level of previously undreamed-of curiosity.

Unfortunately, for me, it was during that spell of mental mystification that the rest of my body decided to raise an arm (my right one I think) and ask a question: a question that most assuredly would scupper any chance that I might have had of endearing myself to the lady with the auburn hair.

"Yes sir?"

"Hello. Um … I was wondering if I was the only person here who actually enjoyed the film for its … entertainment value?"

A silence then fell, like a heavy blanket, across the room. It was as if I had just owned up to being the man who had shot, and then eaten, Donald Duck: and Bambi's mother.

"Excuse me?"

"I just wondered if anyone actually enjoyed the film …" I merrily continued, my brain still engaged elsewhere, "… as a film."

"How do you mean?"

"You know … watched it for watching's sake."

"I'm not following you, sir. In what way do you mean?"

"In ..." It was then that brain and mouth joined up once more. "In the ... er ... the way that one might enjoy, say, a Marx Brothers film. That is."

"Are you English?"

"Yes ..."

"I think we may have hit upon the difference." There was a murmur of laughter and a great deal of nodding heads.

"Why?" I asked. "Hitchcock was English, wasn't he?"

"He ... that is ... he was born in London. Yes. But he became a naturalised American citizen in 1955. May have been 1956. Versions vary."

"Really? So how is it that he was knighted in 1979?"

"Because ... that is ... Okay people, any other questions?"

I felt that perhaps the time had come for me to vacate the small auditorium, and, with as little fuss as possible, I began making my way towards the door.

"You don't have to leave, you know."

I recognised the voice, and I also recognised the fact that it shouldn't really have been anywhere near me. I turned to find the lovely lady with the auburn hair.

"I ... er ... I beg your pardon."

"I said that you don't have to leave."

"No?"

"No."

"Oh. I should have thought my departure was, by now, almost obligatory."

"Not at all. Jeez, those guys could talk all night. And they usually do."

"But ... I thought ... that you ... were ... you know, taking ... doing ..."

"No, I just like to wind them up and then leave them in a deep and meaningful conversation so that I can get to the bar more easily."

"Oh!"

"Would you care for a glass of something?"

"That sounds like a jolly good idea."

"Did I hear you say that you're from England?"

"Indeed you might have."

"That's great."

"I have a tendency to think so."

"Are you living over here?"

"No. Well, not on a permanent basis ... that is."

"No? So how long are you staying in the City?"

"About six weeks."

"On business?"

"No."

"Vacation?"

"Not exactly."

"So ..."

I then took several minutes to explain how I came to be wandering around San Francisco, and what the weeks had in store for me.

"Oh, by the way," I then interrupted myself, "my name is William. William Phalarope."

"Hi William ... pleased to meet you. I'm Gabriella. Gabriella LaQuenta."

"Delighted to make your acquaintance, Gabriella."

During the next - if I may say so – very pleasant few minutes, Gabriella told me that she was due some personal time from work, and would be delighted to show me parts of the City that, as a normal tourist, I might overlook. I was equally delighted to accept her offer. Actually, if I was going to be perfectly honest, I was thrilled to bits.

In the meanwhile I continued with the 'experiment' for the magazine. Jocelyn was telephoning me every few days to ask me questions. Was I enjoying myself? What did I think of San Francisco? Had I made any friends? I was quite sure that what she really wanted to know was if I had attracted the attentions of the local constabulary in any way, and whether or not the magazine

184

was likely to have a large legal fee to settle. I'm not sure my answers did much to assuage her concerns, but there you are.

Was I having fun? Of course I was! It may have taken a bit longer than it might for most people, but there eventually came a time when I was just about getting the hang of moving around the city and finding out where most places of interest were located. Not completely au fait, you understand; just a bit more aware of where certain places were in relation to one another.

Then, as a result of having had a fascination with matters cartographical since I was a pupil in Mr Ruddock's geography class at my prep school, I spent part of one particular morning having a look through my plastic-coated street map of the City.

Mr Ruddock – I wish I could remember his first name. He was of Irish descent, so it could have been Seamus, or Padrig; but I have a feeling it was probably something totally unrelated ... like Walter. Anyway, Mr Ruddock had a passion for maps and, as with most enthusiastic teachers, his passion had a tendency to rub off onto his students: and so it did with yours truly: hence the map in my hands.

I have already mentioned the somewhat uninteresting naming of certain streets and avenues in the City, but I would like to take this opportunity to redress the balance slightly – back in favour of the bizarre.

Listed amongst the names I found the following ...

Belcher Street.
De Boom Street.
Incinerator Road.
Pratt Place.
Nob Hill (the location of the apartment I was using).
Lick Place.
Fella Place.

There were also some locations with rather British connections ...

Bromley, Falmouth, Harlow, Kensington, Greenwich and York. Even a St. George Alley.

But the one that really caught my eye was Hooker Alley; and, as I have been known to enjoy the occasional game of rugby, I felt that it was worth a visit: so I grabbed my camera and hurried away. However, upon my arrival at the supposed location, I found that my map was slightly out of date and that the alley had been boarded-in and claimed, I assumed, by nearby residents.

I imagine that my disappointment – and confusion – must have been apparent, as I was soon approached by a gentleman who was passing by whilst walking a rather small dog.

"May I help you?" he very kindly asked. "You look kinda lost."

"Oh, hello," I replied, always keen to acknowledge unprompted offers of assistance. "Please, yes. I was looking for Hooker Alley."

"Oh really!"

"I thought I might take a photo of the name. For some of my friends."

"Yeah! May I ask why?"

"Of course. I had always wanted to be a hooker when I was at school."

"You did!"

"Yes. But I was a bit too tall. The master in charge always preferred shorter boys. He thought they would make better hookers."

"He did?"

"Indeed. He always used to say that a short boy was better able to hang on to the props than a tall boy."

"Your master made the boys hang on to props!"

"Oh yes. Otherwise – when they bent over – they'd lose their balance."

186

"Oh ..."

"And the shorter the boy was, the easier it was for him to use his feet."

"What! The boy had to use his feet?"

"Absolutely. You weren't allowed to use your hands."

"No hands? But you were allowed to use your feet?"

"As well as having to push at the same time."

"Well I'll be darned."

"Quite. Not all that easy for young boys, I must say."

"Jeez. I ... I can't believe they made young boys do things like that."

"Oh, good heavens yes."

"While they're still at school?"

"In the affirmative once again. In fact, the younger the boy was when he started, the sooner he would be able to pick up all the tricks."

"And this was legal? At school?"

"Naturally."

"I ... well ... What sort of school was it?"

"A Public School."

"One of the British Public Schools?"

"Indeed."

"I had heard about those; but you kinda think that ... well ... you never really know what to believe."

"Well, it wasn't all cold showers and being a fag for the senior boys, you know."

"You were made to be fags as well?"

"Oh yes. A lot of the older boys were rather keen on it. Wanting to keep up the traditions, and so forth. Not quite of the 'Flashman' era, but pretty close."

"And ... are they ... still ..."

"What? At it? Being hookers?"

"Uh-huh ..."

"Good heavens, yes. Friends of mine certainly are, and they must be well into their fifties."

"What! Jeez. Is their much calling for hookers of that age?"

"Oh yes. Well, for certain fixtures. Obviously the old fellows aren't quite as quick, or as flexible, as they used to be; but they're still raring to give it a go."

"And do you ...?"

"Oh, good lord, no. The idea of bending over and having several brawny men pushing me from behind lost its appeal somewhat. And I always felt that at my age and with my build I was quite likely to get injured. I tend to watch mostly these days."

"You like to watch?"

"Absolutely. Mind you, if I was being totally honest, I might admit to a slight yearning to get stuck in there once again."

"That is extraordinary. I just never imagined ..."

"I suppose it might seem a bit peculiar."

"I would say more than just a 'bit'."

"Although in the modern era, most hookers - the ones that do it at the top level that is - are all over six feet tall. And most of them weigh in excess of seventeen stones. And, I'm sure they won't mind me saying, they are a bunch of ugly buggers. Too much for me to compete with. Anyway, I decided that I wanted to keep my looks. Ha!"

"Ha!"

"Ha-ha!"

The man then walked away, slowly shaking his head and muttering something about there should be a law against such things, that he had never wanted to believe any of the stories he had heard about British Public Schools, and that if he had sons he wouldn't dream of ever sending them there.

Peculiar fellow. Anyway, I was unable to take my photograph.

I sample Modern Art.

Gabriella phoned me at the apartment one afternoon and asked if I would like to go and see an exhibition at the San Francisco Museum of Modern Art — or SFMOMA, as she said it was known. To be perfectly honest, I couldn't have cared less if it was known as the William Phalarope is a Twit Museum: it was an opportunity to spend some time in her company, and I thought I could handle an evening of modern art without causing any trouble. However.

Up until that time, it had been my impression that modern art consisted of paintings that didn't really look anything like what had been in front of the painter when he first dabbed his Filbert into a patch of Burnt Umber. Or else it was a sculpture made out of spare bicycle parts and a dead chicken.

Speaking of dead chickens, I went into a Chinese restaurant last night and saw on the menu a course described as 'Healthy Chicken'. Struck me as being a bit odd, I have to say. I mean, how else were the proprietors going to describe it? Apart from 'deceased', that is. I don't suppose there was much chance of them notifying their patrons that the chicken had dropped dead due to an outbreak of Ranikhet, or that it had been suffering from a bad bout of flu. Perhaps one was meant to assume that the chicken, although healthy, had been depressed, and had decided to take its own life by shaking off all its feathers and then leaping into a pre-heated oven.

Anyhow, I turned up outside the entrance to the SFMOMA and eagerly awaited the arrival of Gabriella. I had dressed casually for the exhibition – in other words I wasn't wearing a tie – but even so, I felt strangely over-dressed. Or was I overly strangely-dressed? It certainly looked that way when I made a comparison with the other attendees.

I went and had a good read through the notice on the board and, despite perusing it three times, I couldn't find any reference to the need for wearing garish clothing. After some contemplation, I began to wonder if the opening of art exhibitions was meant to be attended in attire resembling a cross between a fancy-dress party and an AGM of the Oscar Wilde Appreciation Society. Or, perhaps, a living sculpture regarding the perils of getting dressed in the dark ... in somebody else's house. Even Quentin Crisp in his hey-day wouldn't have looked out of place among the gathered patrons, and I began to wonder if the objective of the evening was to admire or to be admired.

I suppose it might be as a result of a flaw in my education, but I do tend to regard someone with what appears to be a pink Wellington boot jammed on their head as being not quite the round shilling. As for what possesses some people to appear in public looking as though they have recently graduated from the 'Bas Couture' school of fashion, I have no idea. Most peculiar, but there we are.

Finally, a ray of sanity shone when Gabriella breezed in; and what a vision she looked too: resplendent in a black, calf-length, pleated skirt, white blouse and navy-blue blazer. Sheer delight, and, if I could have, I would have framed that image and hung it on every wall in the gallery. But that was just my little fantasy. Anyway, we exchanged cordial greetings and went inside.

I don't know your opinion, but I would not describe myself as being anywhere near competent, or knowledgeable, enough to sensibly debate the meaning behind many (most in fact) items of modern art. But, to use an old expression, I know what I like; and, by a simple conclusion, I also know what I don't

190

like: and I knew that I didn't like what I saw in the exhibition. On top of which, apart from having to struggle my way through groups of people that I would really rather not have come within thirty yards of in the course of an average day, I had to endure some of the most incredibly fatuous – to me at any rate – conversations as I did so.

" ... and I have always felt that Abstract Expressionism does not describe any one particular style; rather a general attitude. I see morally loaded themes, often heavyweight and tragic, in grand contrast to the themes of social realism that ..."

" ... represented a reaction against what its members saw as the destruction brought about by the rationalism that guided European culture in the past. I believe that Surrealism is a means of reuniting the conscious with the unconscious realms of experience so absolutely in a blinding vision of ..."

" ... and, of course, the cubists were able to alter art as we knew it. As Wang Pi put it, 'With the idea accomplished, the form can be forgotten'. So just discard traditional forms, make anthropomorphic assumptions, advance in a way that ..."

" ... as being the real difference between the three types of modernism. One should reject the sovereign autonomous individual with an emphasis upon the anarchic collective. Seek out the Dionysian passion and the mystically unrepresentable. Focus on the merging of ..."

Was it any wonder that I felt ill? There was, so it seemed to me, as much bovine excreta (if you'll pardon the expression) being spoken as there was hanging on the walls. Apart from one particular exhibit that is; and that was because it was prepared mostly in elephant dung. Now that exhibit could accurately be described as being a load of complete doo-dah! Apart from the bits that had urine in them. Apparently the artist had 'formulated' an empathy with the two waste products. That piece of information came as no surprise to me. But what do I know?

I did, however, try my best to look interested as Gabriella spoke about the various items that we passed: but it was a

191

struggle. And, I am quite sure, if I had been able – or even wanted to - take my eyes off her for more than a few seconds at a time, I would have passed out from an over-exposure to the aforementioned detritus.

For my own tastes, I like a painting to be a painting. Something done in oils or watercolours: something that I could hang on the wall of my lounge and admire: something that left me in no doubt what it was meant to be. Give me a Turner, or a Constable, or quite a lot of Renoir's work. I particularly like his (Renoir's) painting entitled 'Landscape at Beaulieu' – the one on the Cote d'Azur, that is, rather than anything to do with a certain Lord Montague.

I am also rather taken with Jan-Frans van Dael's 'Flowers before a window': and, to mention others, quite a few by Titian, Verrocchio, Botticelli, and da Vinci as well. Unfortunately, I don't imagine that I shall ever be able to afford any of those! A small section of the frame, possibly: a very small section, that is.

Indeed, give me a hazy depiction of a certain 'Fighting Temeraire' being tugged to her last berth; or a view of Brighton beach, any day.

Speaking of Brighton beach, I still have memories of Sunday exeats from my Prep School, when an uncle and aunt used to take me down to Brighton and let me loose on either the West or the Palace Pier to spend a shilling on the slot machines. For those under the age of forty – or those who, due to the ravages of time, have forgotten - back then there were twelve pennies to the shilling: and that meant twelve goes on the machines.

I was never particularly enamoured with the machine that provided you with spinning lemons whose unpredictable combinations might (and I mean *might*) allow you to recoup some (and I mean *some*) of your outlay. But give me one of those machines that needed a certain amount of tactile skill to flick a metal ball-bearing into a circular maze and bounce off a few nails in such a way that it would fall into a half-round receptacle (thus

192

enabling one to either have another go or win back tuppence) and I was able to make a shilling last for a couple of hours. Unless, that is, I managed to slope off and have a peek in one of those 'What the Butler Saw' machines!

Having said that, what the butler saw back then was rather innocuous when compared with the sort of smut commonly seen these days – even on television advertisements. Why do advertising executives imagine that draping a scantily clad young woman on the bonnet of a car is going to do anything other than draw the eyes of the average heterosexual male away from the car itself? Do I notice that the car has a double overhead cam? No. I do, however, notice that the model has. Do I realise that the car has variable traction control and can get from nought to sixty in 6·3 seconds? No. I do, however, wonder whether any of the leering individuals present were capable of controlling their own traction for more than 6·3 seconds.

So, what have I been noticing? The young lady of course. Maybe the advertisers should consider placing the car in surroundings that divert one's eyes back to the car. Although, considering the inclinations of a goodly percentage of the male inhabitants of certain parts of San Francisco …

Anyway, what fun those exeats were: simple, clean, and oh-so innocent. Lots of schoolboys, all in the same boat (as far as having parents who were many thousands of miles away was concerned) and all impatiently waiting for the Sunday morning chapel service to finish so that they could head to the seaside - if that was where their respective guardians were taking them. A shilling for two hours' amusement. A shilling! Money well spent, I can tell you. Toys and clothes will eventually wear out, but memories can last a lifetime.

Yes, yes, I know that in those days two people could have a meal out, see a show, take a taxi home, and still have change from ten bob: but even so. These days it would probably cost upwards of twenty pounds to keep a ten year-old amused for a couple of hours. Don't you just love progress?

But back to the present. With my ever-reliable source of endurance, I manfully struggled on through the exhibition. I even spent ten minutes trying to understand what a white rectangular board with red markings at the front was meant to represent. Gabriella was kind enough to point out that it was, in fact, the cupboard where a fire hose was stored.

Then I happened upon a section that was entitled – 'A celebration of disability'. Now call me simple-minded by all means, and I've no doubt that there are plenty of people who know me who will be only too willing to endorse that sentiment, but what is there to celebrate about disability? I am quite sure that those who are disabled are in no mood to 'celebrate' the unfortunate hand that Life has dealt them. Are there people who, on a regular basis, raise a glass and rejoice in the fact that they cannot walk? Or have no hands? Or cannot see? Somehow I doubt it.

I can quite see the point of wanting to admire – and, indeed, celebrate - the way that some people are able to overcome impediments of one sort or another. Hats off and a loud round of applause to all of them. But wanting to 'celebrate' disability …?

As much as it embarrasses me to say, I don't think that I possess the fortitude, or determination, to conquer an impediment anywhere near as severe as some that I see surmounted by others. Heavens, I feel at an all-time nadir when stricken by a cold, and demand oodles of attention and sympathy from anyone within hailing distance. Bring on the cosseting, I say: that sort of thing can't be spread too thickly.

I wasn't all that sure if Gabriella was impressed with my attitude on the subject: but if she wasn't, she kept it to herself. You will be pleased to hear that I also showed a sense of propriety as regards my views on people in wheelchairs who 'demand' certain privileges as being a part of a list of inalienable rights. Call me a bit of a bigot, by all means, but I have always been able to distinguish the difference between a 'desire' to have something and a 'right' to have something: and I have always

194

found that cooperation and consideration work far better than coercion. But, yet again, nobody has ever bothered to ask me for my opinion.

Next on my list of potential point-losing moments with Gabriella arrived when she took me into a room that was adorned with photographs that had been taken by a fellow called Charles Lutwidge Dodgson: or Lewis Caroll as he was better known.

I had heard one or two rumours about his predilection for taking photographs of young children, and that his book about Alice was based on a young girl called Alice Liddle for whom he professed a great fondness. Whilst I realise that it is not always appropriate to judge a chap on those points, I must admit to developing a disinclination to want the cove at my dinner table. I must also admit to feeling rather uneasy about the photographs on display, and had to excuse myself from the room after only a couple of minutes.

I might be a tad prudish about such matters, but the subject material in those photographs did not appeal to me on any level. I felt a bit ill, if truth be told. Not that, you understand, any of the photographs on display – at least not those I had seen up to the point that I excused myself – showed any children in less clothing than they might have worn in a public swimming pool: but I don't think that was the issue. It was just that there was something that seemed highly distasteful to me, and I could well imagine the present-day police being informed by the film processors if such images suddenly appeared before them through the developing mixture.

And then I came across the pièce-de-resistance of the show. A six feet by eight canvas that bore – predominantly – two colours, mainly arranged one above the other, and a small legend that mentioned how the background colour was subtly related to those of the two rectangles.

I forget what it was called (should have been 'Two Tone Tat') and by whom it was painted, but I do remember the price attached to it. Two million dollars! And the gallery was so proud to have acquired the painting. I would have been thoroughly ashamed to have it known that so much money had been spent on something that, to my way of thinking, an intoxicated orang-utan could have knocked-up on a particularly wet Friday afternoon in January.

It was, to me, an obscenity; and I said to Gabriella that the two million dollars would have been better spent building another hospital operating theatre and then displaying photographs of those whose lives had been saved as a result.

However, philanthropic aspirations aside for a moment, I managed to blot the old copybook a few minutes later with a sizeable – even by my standards – faux pas.

I had, thanks to constant reminders about vigilance, attuned my awareness of safety in public places to a degree that would have impressed members of the judging panel for the 'Weekly Watchful Awards'. Consequently, it came as no surprise to me that I was the first person to spot the abandoned suitcase that lay in a secluded corner.

With confidence in my ability to stay calm in hazardous circumstances, I strode over to a security guard – he was the second chap I noticed in a uniform: the first was merely wearing one as his choice of apparel for the evening – and, in a voice that was low enough to explain myself without being overheard by those nearby, I brought to his attention the fact that I had spotted an abandoned item of luggage.

What happened next was a mess of frenetic activity, involving a great deal of shouting and whistle-blowing. I can recall people being encouraged to vacate the immediate area as quickly as possible; I can further bring to mind a great deal of commotion as dozens of terrified people then stampeded for the nearest exits.

I, however, remained composed. I pointed to the nearest emergency exits; I told people not to panic; I said that the matter would be dealt with in no time at all: and so it was. In no time at all it was brought to my attention, by a particularly aggressive man pointing what looked like a cattle-prod in my general direction, that the 'abandoned case' was actually one of the exhibits. More money well spent, I have no doubt. Then, in a way that smacked of hostile commercialism, I was further informed that had I bothered to purchase one of the programmes I would have been able to tell that it was by the up-and-coming artist Nathan Brasbaliauskas: or a name similar to that.

"Well," I responded, anxious to stand my ground, "it was a blooming silly place to put it."

"Didn't you notice that it had a spot-light shining on it?"

"That was how I was able to notice it in the first place. And jolly lucky it was too. I might have missed it all together. And then what would have happened?"

My logic, so it seemed, was totally wasted on the assembled posse that I found before me, and, with scarcely any semblance of good manners, I was escorted to the main door and told, in no uncertain terms, never to darken their portals again. Although those weren't the actual words they used, the meaning was the same.

The Columbus Day Parade.

The second Monday in October brings with it the excuse for many San Franciscans to celebrate Columbus Day by parading about between the North Beach and China Town areas of the City. Gabriella asked me if I would like to go along to watch: of course I wanted to!

197

So, off we trundled to find a good vantage point on, unsurprisingly, Columbus Avenue (somewhere between Vallejo and Green as I recall): and what a parade it was. Floats a'plenty, sheriffs on horseback, marching bands, and a group of children who didn't have any instruments but were urged to stamp their feet every six paces by a girl of about 14 who seemed to delight in barking orders. I don't envy the males who are going to be sharing an office with her in ten years' time!

I also saw dancing dustbin-men, a giant fish and a trolley-car that had been, so it advertised, designed by some kind of Sicilian organisation. Did it belong, I thought, to the 'Capo di tutti Capi'? And just in case it did, I declined from taking any photographs. One never knows.

Next, the crowd was treated to the spectacle of some kind of City Official throwing sweets from an open-topped car as he passed by. I can remember noticing that his throwing action was slightly reminiscent of a girl's, and commented to Gabriella that it was just as well he wasn't seeking employment in baseball circles. I don't recall using a volume of voice that would have carried as far as said official, but it certainly appeared as if it might have, for, almost immediately, the car carrying him stopped.

I do recall that my first instinct was to point at the person standing beside me and make facial expressions that would indicate it was he and not I who had spoken. I also recall that my second instinct was to get down on my hands and knees and pretend to look for something. I cannot recall a third instinct as the supervisor then stood up and waved at a lady who was leaning out of a second floor window.

Now, by 'second floor', I mean the second floor above the ground floor. Not, as the Americans (for some reason best known to themselves) call the floor that is one floor above the floor at ground level: which they call the 'first floor'. Highly confusing; especially if, as someone who is accustomed to the nomenclature used in the British Isles, you are trying to get to a particular level whilst pushing buttons in a lift: or elevator.

Anyway, this chap decided, as if to prove me wrong, that he would toss a few of the aforementioned articles of confectionary to the, by now, eagerly awaiting lady at the window. Big mistake.

Using an action that was very much akin to someone trying to throw things whilst having their elbows tied to their waist (rather like, as I have already mentioned, the normal action of a girl), the unfortunate official began to fling the sweets.

The sweets (or candy if you prefer) went to the left of the window, and then they went to the right. They went below the window, they went above: some never even left the confines of the motor vehicle. I have never seen such an inept display of shying since my great aunt Kath (who, I might add, had suffered a minor stroke two months previously) decided to try and win a coconut at a local fête: one of the ones that are often worse than death, as I like to call them.

Out of the four balls she dispatched, two caused the owner of the stall to take evasive action by diving behind the counter, one went forty feet behind her (hitting the judge of the 'best turned out dog' competition on the back of the head), and the fourth one sailed over the top of the stall and was never seen again. Although rumours did circulate that it landed in a coffee urn and was the reason that several local people later went down with an affliction that closely resembled urticaria.

I couldn't help but wonder if the way that the unfortunate discharger's aim went first to the left and then to the right was some kind of metaphor for his ever-changing political inclinations. Perhaps I was being a bit too harsh. Perhaps there was a strong, and inconsistent, crosswind that lurked between the two participating pairs of hands in the scenario. A metaphor for the vicissitudes of life perhaps?

"He's not very good at tossing, is he?" offered Gabriella.

You will be pleased to know that I refrained from replying, "And isn't that strange, because he certainly looks like a tosser to me." Oh yes, we Phalaropes can always be relied upon for our discretion.

But why, I found myself wondering, do Americans celebrate Columbus Day? Christopher (or Cristobal, if you prefer) Columbus – never even saw North America. His first landfall was in the Bahamas (thought by some to be the current San Salvador, but disputed by others who reckon it was more likely Samana Cay), and the only current U.S. territories either sighted or visited by Columbus are the U.S. Virgin Islands (which Columbus named on his second voyage) and Puerto Rico. He later visited the northeast tip of South America and the east coast of Central America, but never reached mainland USA. Furthermore, and all credit to Columbus, he never said that he had.

I suppose that the answer to 'Who discovered America?' rather depends on how far back you choose to look. Go back tens of thousands of years and some Asiatics could probably claim the title. Later, you would hear voices from Basque fishermen, Portuguese, Chinese, Japanese, and even Carthaginians. St. Brendan has a bit of a shout on the subject as well. However, I think that – running the risk of infuriating those of Italian stock – the prize really has to go to a gentleman by the name of Leif Erickson.

The Italians have brought much to this world for which I shall be ever grateful – La Boheme (Puccini), the catapult (Dionysius the Elder), Radio (Marconi), the Jacuzzi (Roy of that ilk), the centrifugal pump (da Vinci), and the telephone (Antonio Meucci). They are, however, also the people who brought us Liposuction (Dr Giorgio Fischer), Nitro-glycerine (Ascanio Sobrero), and the space-hopper (Aquilino Cosani). But discover America they did not: so we can't blame them for that. Back to the parade.

Splendid stuff. Mind you, I did feel a bit sorry for the kids. It was a swelteringly hot day, and marching for a couple of hours in it probably wasn't at the top of their 'Things I must do today' list. Roll on next year?

200

<u>The World Series.</u>

Whilst I was over in San Francisco there was a bit of a baseball competition going on - The World Series. I, amongst many others no doubt, have always thought that 'World Series' is a bit of a misnomer, as the competition isn't often open to outsiders. But I feel I should emit a very loud 'Hurrah' for the Toronto Blue Jays ('92 and '93) at this point.

I have heard people mention that the reason why other countries are not invited to take part in the tournament is the fact that the seasons are wrong – when the US is ending its season, the rest are just starting – but that doesn't seem to cause any problem with the soccer brigades. Point out this fact and they say that there aren't enough other countries playing baseball. Well, in a true 'World Series', the US would have just one team – the 'USA' one - and since at least a quarter of the players in last year's world series were born overseas, I would imagine that one or two other countries could easily provide a team.

Some people say that nobody wants to take part. Well, I suppose that's also because nobody ever seems to get asked. Another 'Hurrah' for the Blue Jays.

"Can't be done," comes another shout. Then perhaps someone could explain how, every year since 1947, the Little League 'world series' has been played? In 2001 there were teams from 50 US states and 103 other countries. That, I would say, is what a 'World Series' should be about. But, yet again, nobody asked me.

Anyway, to return to my trip, the 2002 final was between the San Francisco Giants and the Anaheim Angels from Los Angeles: and quite an exciting final it turned out to be. Although, as a final, it was the best of seven games: and each game had nine innings for each team: and each etc. etc: and Anaheim won 4-3. Ah well.

I didn't manage to get to see any of the games live, although I did watch a bit on television, but Gabriella took me down to Pacific Bell Park while one of the games was going on inside. Apparently the tickets were as expensive as precious stones and as rare as hens' teeth.

There was, however, an advert – in some publication or another, although it might have been on a web-site – for a pair of tickets (for the series) in exchange for a donation of ... er, I'm not sure I can put this delicately? ... some semen! I kid you not.

The holders of the tickets – two ladies (hailing from the Isle of Lesbos I should imagine) - were willing to exchange said tickets for said 'donation'. Natural curiosity encouraged me to read a bit more, and I discovered that the transaction was not going to be a simple exchange. Oh no. There was a list of conditions – about as long as an EU Directive – that stipulated exactly how, when, and where the business was to be carried out; what sort of person the donor was to be – height, colour, intellect etc. – their medical history and lineage; that there was to be no contact after the 'fertilisation' – which was to take place in vitro (rather than in vivo), and that the donor was to have no claim on, or contact with, the progeny, unless the ladies were of a mind to allow it to happen.

As for the selection of affidavits that had to be signed ... Well, I doubt if the poor fellow would have had a hand free long enough to fulfil his part of the arrangement.

Needless to say, I declined the opportunity. Although I did imagine, had he taken up the offer, that Julius Caesar might have slightly curtailed his original quote, and simply said "Veni, vidi."

While the game was going on, Gabriella and I took a stroll around the stadium, and found - to the south side – in the water, an armada of small boats, surfboards and pedalos that had assembled there. Great fun appeared to be the order of the day; with a lot of noise, light, laughter and expectant expressions on the people there gathered.

I asked Gabriella why those people should have chosen a damp venue for their meeting; rather than, for instance, the perfectly adequate jetty on which I was standing. It transpired that the assemblage had chosen that location as it was the area where, should a certain Barry Bonds choose to hit a home run, the baseball was most likely to come to rest. And, whether for reasons of financial gain or kudos, they would make every effort to seize the ball.

Apparently such a jamboree was a pretty regular occurrence whenever B. Bonds Esq. was in town and wielding a bat: and an occasion such as that was this: and quite an occasion it was too. An impressive array of craft was there for me to behold – already mentioned – and a good time was being had by all. We stood, watched and waited for about a half of an hour, in the hope that one of the baseballs would – accompanied by a tumultuous roar from within the stadium – descend from out of the floodlit night, and cause the flotilla to positively be set alight with frenzy.

Unfortunately no such ball arrived; but a certain amount of setting alight did take place, nonetheless. I had, several minutes previously, noticed a pedalo, containing two men, that was circling just outside the throng. I had also observed, on the back of the pedalo, an object that I thought was some kind of engine.

Bravo, I thought, men who were concerned about the conservation of energy, principally their own, and perhaps they had had to travel some distance to attend the festivities.

It came as little surprise, therefore, when I later saw their craft positively whizzing through the water with what appeared to be flames issuing from the stern. *Jet propelled?* I further postulated. But I was mistaken. Not about the flames though: they were real enough. It seemed that the object I thought was an engine was, in fact, a barbeque that the men had fixed on the pedalo with, I presumed, the intention of furnishing themselves with all manner of hot meat products.

However, as a certain R. Burns once put it ... 'The best laid plans of mice and men, gang aft a-gley': and the plans in this case had really ganged a-gley; and in rather a spectacular fashion as well.

It appeared that the barbeque had ignited with a bit more enthusiasm than originally planned, and was now burning away like a barn on fire: and, especially if you are sitting less than two feet away from said conflagration, that is not a cause for unbridled merriment. It is, however, a cause to pedal as fast as you can entice your lower members to perform: and that was what we were witnessing. I was most impressed, I must say.

Judging by the round of spontaneous applause that emanated from the rest of the convoy, I think it met with unanimous approval.

To return to the Giants' downfall: I think the mourning could well have been tempered by the fact that the San Francisco Giants originally came from New York, and began in 1883 when – under the name of the New York 'Gothams' - they joined the National League. They won the 'World Series' in 1905, 1921, 1922 and 1954, and moved to San Francisco in 1958. But I'm not here to give you a history lesson. However, I will make mention that I believe the game originated from 'Rounders', and that American Football started from Rugby League. Actually, come to think of it, pretty much every sport in the world either began or was codified in Britain. Impressive, eh?

"But so what?" I said, whilst on the subject of baseball and American Football, to the enormous fellow who seemed rather displeased that I had brought up the subject whilst enjoying a bottle of a local brew in a small hostelry nearby. "Everything has to start somewhere."

"So what!" came the reply.

What is it about Americans that makes them go all defensive (and aggressive) whenever you question their self-proclaimed immutable right to feel superior to everyone else they meet? Almost to the point of solipsism. Do they all belong to a solipsist society? Or is that a contradiction in terms?

Anyway, all I did was point out the fact that, as I understood it, two of their national games had their roots in my part of the planet. A simple enough observation, I would have thought. But apparently it wasn't.

"How dare you come over here and tell me – a citizen of the greatest country on earth – that you started our national games. Huh?"

"Well, we did."

"Oh yeah. Says who?"

"Well, it sounded very much like *my* voice."

"A smart-ass, huh?"

"Thank you for noticing. Anyway, I think you will find that Rugby – generally attributed to the antics of one William Webb Ellis – started around 1823. I also believe you will find that – by way of 'ballown' and an annual event known as 'Bloody Monday' – interest in your form of the sport didn't really achieve notice until around 1860. Now, and I'm sure you will correct me if I'm wrong, I am under the impression that 1823 precedes 1860 by more than thirty-five years. Res ipsa loquitor."

"Eh?"

"Quite."

"Well, what about your – what's it called? – crocket?"

"I think that you may be getting one of the finest games – often described as a metaphor for life – muddled up with a gentleman from Tennessee who, apart from laying down his life at the Alamo, is best remembered for walking around with a dead animal stuck on the top of his head. A procedure that, I hasten to add, wouldn't produce the individual status quite so effectively if used in present-day, downtown San Francisco. Cricket, sir, is the word for which you are searching: and, before you even attempt to make a comparison, it is nothing like baseball."

"No sireebob it sure ain't."

"And for that the rest of the civilised world will always be grateful."

How can one ever hope to get the finer points of cricket across to someone who judges if a game is to be worth watching by the amount of food he can shovel down his throat between whistles? Come to think of it, that is probably why games like rugby and soccer have never really taken off in the States. They don't last long enough to allow spectators sufficient time to finish a wheelbarrow full of popcorn/hotdogs/ice-cream and enough fizzy drink to fill a bath. It's strange that five-day test match cricket hasn't caught on!

Anyway, just in case anybody is under the impression that I, alone, am having a go at the eating habits of Americans, perhaps I can draw your attention to an observation made by Charles Dickens – around 1842 – whilst he was in the USA.

He wrote of how there would always be a huge glass of cranberries on the table at dinner; and that breakfast would have, as its principal dish, a deformed beefsteak (the T-bone was, as yet, unknown in the UK) swimming in hot butter and sprinkled with black pepper.

Speaking of which, don't you just want to roar with laughter when, usually in a middle-of-the-range type of restaurant, some rather loud fellow at an adjacent table orders

206

(often employing a piercing volume that is sufficient to let those in an adjacent street know) a bottle of something fairly expensive – say a Chateau Latour - and then, in an unfathomable desire to add a lack of intelligence and good taste to his already apparent lack of good manners, he goes ahead and orders steak au poivre.

Now I might be wrong, but I have always supposed that a good wine was meant to be savoured and enjoyed; and not forced to compete with taste-bud-destroying lumps of hot pepper.

To return to Dickens, he mentioned – in Martin Chuzzlewit – the amount of food that was usually laid out on tables, and the extraordinary lengths to which gentlemen would go in their endeavours to push said food down their throats. Not a pleasant image, as I recall.

Even the Count of Volney once wrote that Americans deserved first prize for a diet sure to destroy teeth, stomach and health; and advised the government, for the good of the country, that they should undertake an educational programme to teach Americans how to eat!

As a further consideration, apart from the shortness of ingesting time, I also think that the rules of rugby might be a bit too complicated for those who spectate hereabouts.

Speaking of rules, I sat and watched as Anaheim pitchers threw the baseball around one of the hitters – the aforementioned Barry Bonds, in fact – in the San Francisco Giants team. By pitching 'around', I mean that they threw the baseball so wide of Mr Bonds that the poor fellow had no chance of being able to hit it.

"What of it?" I expect you just asked. Well, this meant that Mr Bonds couldn't hit any home runs; and the reason why they persisted with this tactic against Mr Bonds is because Mr Bonds has a habit of hitting home runs – 73 of the things in the 2001 season, which was some kind of a record I believe.

I have to say that it smacks of cheating to me. Or, at the very least, unsportsmanlike behaviour.

"Why," I asked one of the rather large-bellied gentlemen in the bar, "don't they create a law akin to the one which concerns 'wides' in cricket."

"The what?" came the reply.

I took a moment or two to explain how it is deemed to be somewhat against the spirit of the game if the bowler bowls a ball that is beyond the reach of the batsman; and how, as a result and as a means of dissuading the bowler from continuing with said display of unsportsmanlike behaviour, the batting side is awarded one run and the fielding side is made to bowl an extra ball. I, with my admittedly limited knowledge of the nuances of baseball, felt that if those responsible for amending the laws of the game adopted a similar rule it would encourage the pitching side to uphold a semblance of fair play, and then winning (if that was to be the outcome) would be without taint.

I took the bemused expressions around me as an indication that the concept had passed high above the top of most of the heads present.

The gathered ensemble of listeners also found the idea of the crowd throwing back any balls that may have landed in their midst – as happens in rugby, soccer or cricket – as too bizarre for further comment. Chacun à son goût, I suppose.

Whilst I'm on the subject of American Football, I stayed up one year to watch the 'Super Bowl' on television in the UK, and was astonished at how little actual play took place. Stop start, stop start. A game with about eighty minutes allotted playing time, and it took over four hours to complete! Give me a game of rugby union any day. None of that interruption nonsense, or any of that palaver when the 'offensive' and 'defensive' teams swap over each time the opposition gets the ball. What on earth is that all about?

Make sure the players are fit enough, and capable of being proficient in both attack and defence is what I say. It would certainly make the game move along more fluidly, and cut down the running costs of the team a fair bit as well I have no doubt. Or

208

am I inadvertently drawing attention to the extensive eating time of the spectators and the limited learning capabilities of the players? Hmm.

I wish good luck to the Giants in the future.

The Candide Operetta.

One evening Gabriella asked, as she knew I liked opera, if I might enjoy a display of chanting by a small, but reputedly fairly good, company that went by the proud name of Goat Hall Productions: which made sense, as Goat Hall was where they held their productions.

The company, apparently in its fifth season, was a theatre community of musicians, actors, designers, and technicians who were dedicated – as the pamphlet I was handed at the door described – to the collaborative creative process. Not quite sure what that meant, but it sounded impressive all the same.

They, so further perusal informed me, presented musical theatre and opera in English, focusing on 20th and 21st century repertoire, at affordable prices and the highest artistic level they could reach. All of which, I'm sure you'll agree, was a more promising foreword than saying they were going to charge the earth for the privilege of watching utter rubbish.

And so, with a smile and an almost jaunty stride, I entered the hall: and that was exactly what it was: a hall. *Ah well, nil desperandum*, I thought to myself, as I manoeuvred my way past a couple of males who were dressed in garb that could well have allowed them to blend in quite nicely with the cast of a camp production of 'Bugsy Malone'.

Difficult to imagine? Let me help you. One of them was wearing black plastic trousers, knee-length leather boots (into which the trouser legs had been tucked), a black shirt, a white tie, and a trilby that looked as though someone may have sat on it. His companion had a pair of trousers that could have (and may well have) been made from lounge curtains, a black shirt and red tie, a beard that seemed slightly off-centre, and a padlock hanging from one of the belt loops on the trousers. Needless to say, I tried not to risk eye-contact.

Gabriella soon found a brace of vacant seats and, with a rising sense of anticipation (or dread, I couldn't be sure) we awaited the commencement of the show: which, incidentally, was 'Candide' – adapted, with music by Leonard Bernstein and lyrics by Richard Wilbur, from the rather amusing book by Voltaire. Although, if some historians are correct, the origins of 'Candide' lie in the 1686 'Discourse on Metaphysics' by Gottfired Leibnitz who, when faced with the problem that all philosophers inevitably have to face – why, if the world was created by an omnipotent, benevolent creator, is there so much evil in the world? - answered that there actually is no evil, and that the fault lies with our perception.

Of course it does.

Anyhow, there we were, awaiting the 'curtain up' to show the stage. Except that there was no curtain: and no stage either. Well, not a *real* stage - just a raised platform sort of thing. But there were stage lights, hanging from some kind of gantry, that adequately lit the area where the main protagonists were about to display their talents. And, because the hall was no more than about sixty feet by fifty, everybody would have an adequate view. Everybody, that is, except me.

I am not sure what it is in my make-up that encourages complete strangers – especially those who are taller than me - to come and occupy a position that is directly in my line of vision. Or if they are the proud possessor of an inconsiderate habit (such as wishing to eat crisps, or sweets that are individually wrapped in at least a square foot of grease-proof paper) they take the seat directly behind mine.

210

I have tried examining myself from all angles before leaving the house in order to make sure that some jolly japester has not stuck a sign on my back that reads 'Please annoy'. I have undergone retrogressive hypnosis to ascertain if some untoward incident during my mother's pregnancy may have affected my psyche. I have even tried being the only person in the cinema when the show started: but to no avail. Somehow I always manage to attract some persona non grata: and tonight was no exception.

No sooner had I taken my seat, than a woman - who as she approached seemed normal enough so I didn't have any immediate cause for concern - came and sat down in front of me. As I said, from a distance she appeared pretty much as Nature had intended; but as soon as her gluteus maximus muscles hit the seat, her affliction became apparent.

The unfortunate woman appeared to have been born with six extra vertebrae. This condition had hitherto been disguised by a clever arrangement of her jacket; so I would never have guessed that of the five and a half feet of her vertical dimension, at least four were taken up by her backbone. Really quite extraordinary.

Next, after a few wiggles, she ran her fingers through her hair and produced an effect the like of which I hadn't seen since 'Pimpley' Perkins had a slight miscalculation with a rheostat that was attached to the electricity mains during one of the physics practical classes at my old school. The net result was rather like having to watch the show through a hedge.

On top of which, as if determined to make my evening complete, the lady decided that viewing the production would be greatly enhanced by swaying from side to side during the musical numbers. So there I was, having to sway from side to side – in time, but in an opposite direction to her - to get a sporadic glimpse of the action and, I'll have you know, beginning to feel more than a touch of mal-de-mer.

Then, if all that wasn't enough malchance for a fellow, the gods of Kleine Leiden must have thought that I was about due for a rather large helping of the stuff because they, very kindly, arranged for four male members of the San Francisco 'Tittering Society' to come and sit directly behind me. Made me feel distinctly scratchy, I don't mind telling you.

But were the members of the SFTS content to merely make me feel uncomfortable? No. They must have thought that I would enjoy the show much more if they proceeded to demonstrate their affection for one another by holding hands, hugging at every opportunity, laughing in a most peculiar fashion, wearing starched smiles, and saying "Oh ... my ... guard" at every available opportunity.

I struggled on, determined to enjoy the evening regardless; though I have to admit that my full appreciation was somewhat hampered by the conductor and one of the ladies in the chorus.

The former, dressed in what I can only assume was meant to be normal attire of the mid-eighteenth century, was jumping up and down on one leg, whilst swinging the other one from side

212

to side, and waving his arms about as if their control had been entrusted to someone with a grudge against a nest of wasps that had taken an interest in relocating to their hair. In fact, had you put him in a suitable leotard, he could well have been running an aerobics class for people suffering from some kind of attention deficit disorder.

And then there was the lady in the chorus. Now, even taking into account the distance between us, the fact that she was under the glare of the lights, and that I was looking through a hedge, it did seem as though she was giving me the 'glad eye'. Flattering to some, I've no doubt; and under different circumstances I may well have felt similarly privileged. Unfortunately, at the same time, the lady was giving her other eye to someone about twenty feet to my left.

I am quite sure that there are plenty of men who could overlook such a minor blemish in an otherwise very attractive lady; but I, sorry to say, am not amongst their number. It just seems slightly off-putting that in order for our eyes to meet in one of those moments of unchecked passion, I would almost certainly have to be in two places at once. I know such things might be possible in Quantum Physics, but I have no wish to possess the attributes of a quark.

However, apart from those minor hiccoughs, the show was great fun; and I shall always roundly applaud those who devote their time and energy to such endeavours. For my own part, prancing about on a stage has never appealed: not just because I cannot sing, or act, or that I come out in a dreadful rash whenever anything resembling make-up comes near my skin; but because I still have memories of being made to take part in a Shakespearean play when I had reached the tender age of seven.

The play was 'A Midsummer-Night's Dream', and the part I was given was that of Snout, the Tinker. I was to make my first entrance – in Act I, Scene II – with Quince, Snug, Bottom, Flute and Starveling; and my opening line was to have been "Here, Peter Quince."

213

Simple enough, one would have thought: but one would not have taken into account two salient factors. The first, my mother: the second, that the school - run by a Miss Scrimshaw, in Calcutta — did not have a sack-load of funds to run a lavish production, or sufficient pupils from which to choose a full cast of children who could remember enough words to keep the play going without constant prompting by a certain Ashley Grimes (one of the teachers) who had a great predilection for pink gins; and, as a result, an equally great tendency to slur his speech.

The first of those two factors resulted in me (because dear mother felt that if I was to play a tinker I should be festooned in pots and pans) coming onto the stage accompanied by such a cacophony that my opening line (and many others) went completely unnoticed. This meant that 'Quince' didn't hear what I said, or that I had actually said anything, and subsequently missed his response.

And that engaged the second part of the second factor: which meant that Mr Grimes was jolted into action. No immediate cause for panic, you might think: until you remember the pink gin partiality. Quince's next line should have been ...

"You, Pyramus' father: myself, Thisby's father. Snug, the joiner; you, the lion's part: and, I hope, here is a play fitted."

A line that, even under the soberest of conditions, would make you think carefully about enunciation; and a line that, when several sheets are loudly flapping about in the wind, can produce all manner of gibberish: and did.

"You ... yoo-hoo ... Hamuses fatter me whoooo ... This ... this bee's fatter ... fitter than snuggles the lion's farter. And, I hop ... yes I do ... a plit flatter hippy hop and a -"

The rest of the sentence was lost as Mr Grimes had decided that getting to his feet would make him more audible. That part of the idea made sense. Pulling on the stage curtain to help him do so, however, did not. The rather flimsy supporting rod – already under excess strain - was immediately pulled from its struts, and lost no time at all in descending, with a thump that could be heard from the other side of the adjacent maidan (you may have to look up that word – pronounced mydown - so I'll save you some time by saying that, in India, it means an expanse of open ground) upon the dome of the aforementioned Mr Grimes.

The expletives that followed are probably best left to the imagination, and I shall be forever grateful that Puck was not involved in the scene.

But, to return to Candide, the deities responsible for my discomposure had one last card to play. At the end of the performance, the men who were sitting immediately behind Gabriella and me, 'whooped and hollered' at each of the play's participants as they came back into view to take their bows.

The four saved their most enthusiastic 'Yohs', 'Yeahs', and 'Whoo-hoos' for the chap who had played the part of Candide – a fellow with the intriguing name of Eric Mutzgobber - and their vocal appreciation barely matched the vigorous clapping that accompanied it.

I, naturally, began to wonder if the five gentlemen were, in some way, acquainted. I had noticed that 'Candide' had been wearing an inordinate amount of make-up, and I could recall that his passage from one side of the stage to the other had been conducted with a certain amount of hip-swivelling. On top of which, I was under the impression that a good proportion of thespians have a bit of a reputation for being active in social spheres and practices about which I wish to know as little as possible. So I had, equally naturally, assumed that the gentleman who played Monsieur Candide would have been more interested in flower-arranging than, say, activities of a grid-iron nature.

But I was mistaken. No sooner had Monsieur Candide taken a couple of bows, than he dashed across to Madame Cunegonde and embarked on as committed a bout of lip wrestling as I have seen in many a long year. My initial surprise was soon overtaken by a wave of 'Ehs?', 'Uhs?' and 'Tsks' that washed over me from behind. It seemed that four daydreams had been cruelly dispelled.

However, three cheers for the Goat Hall Productions.

A Stroll down Market Street

During my stay in the City, I had several opportunities to take a walk along a thoroughfare known as Market Street. A little over four miles long, it runs in a diagonal direction – from bottom left to top right of the City as you look from above – across the middle of San Francisco, and separates the Castro, Mission and SOMA (South of Market) districts from the Lower Haight, Hayes Valley, Tenderloin and China Town districts.

When I first mentioned my intention to walk along Market Street, Gabriella suggested that perhaps I might care to make it more of a jog. A sprint would be even better. Apparently it's not the sort of place where one ought to tarry any longer than necessary; if at all: especially where it meets Sixth Street. Unpleasant people, she went on to say, tend to congregate in that area.

Unfortunately, the Phalaropes have long been known for sailing their own ships: or, as many other people have been known to comment, for ignoring advice and generally doing things as they see fit. So off I toddled.

I began my amble at the Civic Centre BART station, and headed in a north-easterly direction towards the Embarcadero (the road that runs alongside the San Francisco Bay and on which all the piers are located), and I soon realised what Gabriella had meant.

About every twenty yards or so I was approached by some mendicant or another, who seemed intent that I should make a contribution to a worthy cause: namely his own. I have to admit to finding this 'face-on' approach a little bit intimidating - to begin with anyway – and little bit mystifying, as I was situated within a quarter of a mile of all the opulence associated with the City Hall, the Symphony Hall, and the Opera House. It didn't seem to make much sense.

It was also a bit perplexing trying to correlate the obvious squalor in which those poor unfortunates found themselves with the plethora of shiny stretch limousines that quietly cruised by; their occupants anonymously hidden behind smoked windows. It seems San Francisco, a city with a population of around 730,000 could boast nearly 8,000 homeless people as well. In other words, around one person in ninety is without accommodation.

It would not be my place to start a protracted discussion of the whys and wherefores they are there, so I won't. Briefly, and obviously, from a climatic point of view, it's less hard on a person being outdoors in a warm environment than in, say, Chicago; but the other reasons are many and varied: and so were the sorts of people I encountered.

Again, I do not wish to castigate San Francisco, and not being a regular visitor to other cities I am in no position to draw comparisons. I am quite sure that London – especially with the colossal influx of bogus refugees and undesirable immigrants over the last few years – would fare no better: except that the vagrants

I met in San Francisco nearly all spoke good English. London, however, can lay claim to one person in fifteen having no command of the English language whatsoever, and one in three not even being born in the country. Comforting statistics? I think not.

Anyway, before I reached the place where I found out – from (authorised) inscriptions in the paving stones – that I was at a longitude of 122°-24 -45 1 , and a latitude of 37°-46 -48 3 , I had bumped into quite a variety of people: including a vociferous gentleman with an accent that seemed to hail from South Carolina.

"Hey, mister," he yelled in my general direction, waving a Bible at me.

I looked from side to side, behind me, and then, with raised eyebrows, I looked back at the man whilst pointing at my chest.

"Yeah, buddy … you."

"Er … yes," I said, as I cautiously approached him.

"Are you a Guard-fearen mayan?"

It took me a moment to decipher what he had said: and I have to admit that I didn't know much about fearing God. Although quite why anyone should feel the need to fear a loving god I don't know. Be in awe of, by all means: but fear? Strange concept. I had to admit, however, to feeling a rapidly rising degree of trepidation towards my newfound quizmaster. "I might be," I replied. "From time to time."

"Gird," he shouted, through what I perceived to be two dead squirrels that had had the singular misfortune to die upon his top lip. "'Cos eye ayam here to saive ah souls."

"Oh."

"Do yooo thie-ink that's a good eye-dee-yer?"

"I … er … Sorry, to save …?"

"Ah souls."

"Oh. Isn't that slightly discriminatory?"

"Huh?"

"I simply thought that it might be rather nice to save everybody; instead of just concentrating on one type of person."

"Huh?"

"I would have thought that all of us, regardless of social status or intelligence, might benefit from your intention. I might be wrong, of course, and I would be the first person to hold up my hand and admit to having misgivings about certain individuals. Especially around these parts. But I suppose that we all have to play the cards with which we have ... been ..."

The growing look of bewilderment – tinged with, I began to feel, a noticeable amount of displeasure - on the face of God's Market-and-Seventh representative encouraged me to begin backing away. With a tap on the face of my watch, a shrug of my shoulders and a sympathetic frown, I turned and carried on with my stroll.

I say stroll, but it was really more akin to rugby practice. So many people; all in a hurry, all with a mobile phone in one hand and a coffee in the other, and nobody really paying attention to anybody else.

And then, as I mentioned, there were all the homeless. I did, maybe foolishly, take the time to sit and talk with a few of them and discovered, much to my surprise, that they weren't the loathsome reprobates I had been inclined to imagine. Of course, some of their number looked particularly unsavoury - and I wasn't of a mind to talk to them, or those who were indulging in activities that involved small packets of tin-foil - so my random sample might not have been all that random. However, the individuals with whom I chose to converse came across as otherwise reasonable people who, as a result of one misfortune or another, happened to find themselves down on their uppers. It was all very sad, and left me feeling both hopelessly inadequate and, as regards my own circumstances, immensely grateful. I do hope that Renée is faring well.

But I was rather confused by the way that a number of young men who - as far as one's initial impression went - appeared to have rather limited access to funding, and yet had managed to find enough of the readies to purchase shoes that, apart from having more 'extras' than an average family saloon, could well have cost as much. However, despite feeling the need to perambulate in footwear that would have enabled them to run like a gazelle, they appeared to not know how to tie up the laces and they also felt an urge to wear trousers that would have tripped them up within three strides.

I ask you, what is the point of wearing a pair of trousers that has a crutch which hangs down below the knees? Unless, of course, those gentlemen were in possession of organs of procreation that hung down just as far. One doesn't really like to enquire about such attributes; especially with a complete stranger. Or perhaps it was thought stylish to walk in the same manner as an intoxicated penguin.

I was later led to understand that the liking for such an appearance stemmed from the fact that incarcerates in various penal establishments are made to remove their belts (and shoelaces) in order to make suicide by hanging a tad more difficult. But the desire to continue with this mode d'habiller when one has attained release is, to me, rather harder to understand. And I can't imagine it would be all that helpful at a job interview.

But the strangest fellow that I had occasion to meet was down at the California Street cable-car turnaround, near the Embarcadero. I didn't manage to elicit his name, but he seemed to spend most of the day perched - and I do mean 'perched' - on a bench, shouting out short sentences that he repeated throughout the day. I couldn't quite make out what he was saying, but good authority told me that it was usually the news headlines, and that they were changed on a daily basis.

He seemed harmless enough, so I never had any hesitation in sharing his bench to read a newspaper while I waited for a cable-car to take me back up to Nob Hill. But on one particular day I was in for a bit of a surprise. I had been waiting for about ten minutes, and listening to his intermittent salvoes of invective that appeared to be aimed at the, then, governor of California (or somebody close to him) for either voting for or against an invasion of Iraq (I was unsure which – or even which invasion) when we made eye-contact. My heart was on the point of making its way towards my throat when the chap smiled, leaned forward, and, with an articulate voice, spoke to me.

"Excuse me, sir," he said, "do you have the time?"

I proffered the face of my watch so that he might establish the time for himself.

"Thank you very much," was his response.

"Ah ... um ... ooh," was, to my eternal chagrin, mine.

Do I have any explanation for the man's conflicting characteristics? None whatsoever, I'm afraid. The Phalaropes have never displayed any flair in the human observation department, so I am somewhat at a loss for offers of sensible reasons. Perhaps, in the words of a rather astute philosopher – whose name escapes me at the present – "Some things just are."

Whilst I have raised the subject of why some things 'just are', my mind has, once again, leapt into the subject area concerning politicians. I have always thought that we (in the UK) had cornered the market on inadequates, such has been the dearth of statesmen in the past twenty or so years. I won't elaborate on why I reflect as I do, but, suffice it to say, I do not want to be controlled by a bunch of unelected, unaccountable beaurocrats whose sole aim seems to be reducing Great Britain to a soulless haven for destitutes and criminals.

As for an explanation regarding the vigour with which they are trying to split up the United Kingdom, I can only assume that the politicians are pursuing the 'Divide and Rule' maxim. Scoundrels to a man, in my opinion. Or perhaps it is in pursuit of the 'New World Order' of which I have heard talk. Now, am I going to spend time on topics such as 'Novus Ordo Seclorum'? No. Strange that that particular expression should be on the dollar bill, isn't it? And as for the horned owl ...

Mind you, it might be of interest if you were to look up the details and aims of a society that derived its title from a chap by the name of Quintus Fabius, and then check out how many members of the UK Parliament belong to it. Rather disconcerting, if you ask me. Work for the State, be dependent upon the State, and be controlled by the State. What was that saying? A system that can provide you with everything you want can also take away everything you have. Mind you, if you think that the Fabian Society is cause for concern, then you will certainly want to avoid discovering what you can about the Bilderberg Group. Or the Georgia Guidestones!

However, California has politicians of its own. While I was in San Francisco some elections were imminent, and I was nightly bombarded through the television screen with a plethora of advertisements for each of the candidates that informed me how corrupt/nefarious/greedy/asinine all the other candidates were: and very little mention of what they were actually going to do. Yes, I remember thinking, so what's new?

What was that old Latin expression? Oh yes, 'Quam parvus sapienta mundus regitur'. With how little wisdom the world is governed. Could have been penned last week, couldn't it? Worth remembering next time you vote. Perhaps we should have a box to tick that reads 'None of the above'.

Anyway, one of the main differences I noticed between San Francisco elections and those in my part of the world was in the ballot paper. What a lot of 'propositions' there were! It seemed that everybody was being asked to vote on every issue.

In the lettered propositions people were asked for their opinions on ...

Water Bonds
Affordable Housing Bonds
Veterans Building Bonds
Energy
Water & Sewer rates, Surplus Funds
Entertainment Commission Appointments
Elections Assistance
Police & Fire-fighter Retirement Benefits
Paid Parental Leave
Supervisors Salaries (and sweet throwing lessons?)
Selection of Official Newspapers
Real Estate Tax
Economic Development
Adjusting Services and Payments to Homeless Individuals
Conditions for Providing Services and Payments to Homeless Individuals
Revenue Bond Oversight Committee
Use of City Funds
Condominium Conversion with Certain Conditions
Medical Marijuana
BART Seismic Safety Bond

... and that was as well as all those propositions that came with numbers. I understand that people have been known to cancel their annual holiday in order to complete the voting slip.

All the citizens of San Francisco have to receive two sets of pamphlets, outlining what all the propositions are about. I say 'pamphlets', but they are really closer to a telephone directory in construction and size: and, so I was led to understand, they have to be printed in various different languages. Now call me old-fashioned if you must, but I have always felt that if you were going to vote in a particular country you really ought to be fully conversant in the language of that country. Might be rather nice if they started to use that format in the UK. Do you think they'll ever get round to doing that? Ha!

Mind you, I also think that people ought to be able to write the name of their preferred candidate – without merely copying it – whilst they are in the voting booth. Although I am quite sure that several of the parties back in the UK would be putting forward candidates who had recently changed their names to Mr X, Y or Z.

But, if all the adverts I heard were to be believed, the voters seemed only to have a choice between a crook and a con-man. So why, as I mentioned earlier, can't voting slips have a box marked 'None of the Above'? Then, as you would if you were conducting interviews for a position at your firm, if none of the candidates was up to the mark, you would merely re-advertise and interview some more: and keep doing so until you found someone who was suitable.

Perhaps that suitable person was the gentleman who spent a great deal of time carrying around a placard that had a lot of writing on it: such as ...

12 GALAXIES IMPEACH CLINTON
DELONGATION OF TERM
NO PARDON
EXPRESSIONENTAL VARGON VISIT

No, it didn't make any sense to me either. The fellow is one of those well-known local personalities; and at the Halloween street party there were several people walking behind him, all dressed the same, all walking with a slightly peculiar sideways shuffle (for those of a certain disposition, the action is known as to 'hirple' – verb intransitive – and rhymes with purple!) and all carrying placards with similar undecipherable slogans. Great fun!

I had thought of going as Oofty Goofty: I might have earned a bob or two, but probably not enough to cover all my hospital bills.

Is it really any of my business what sort of individual gets elected in California? Not really I suppose, unless they get elected to high office and influence decisions made in the UK. Oops, a bit too late to worry on that score! And, as a rather astute fellow – whose name I forget – once said "People get the government they deserve." But what I would like to know, is what crime did I commit to end up with the calamitous clodpates who hold sway in my neck of the wood? Something else from that previous life, I expect.

Cable-Cars.

One of the main attractions of San Francisco is the cable-cars. What marvellous contraptions they are, with quite a history; and I have to say that I did enjoy going on them - whether as an interested tourist or like a child on a fairground ride I wasn't sure. The cars are expensive to make, expensive to run, have a tendency to bewilder and infuriate car drivers (especially when they stop in the middle of junctions – the only flat bits), and safety is not at the forefront of passenger consideration. But they are jolly good fun all the same: and travelling on them can, apparently, sometimes be financially rewarding and enable you to perk up a lagging libido.

"I beg your pardon!" I hear you exclaim. "Perk up a lagging libido? What are you on about?"

In 1964, a jury awarded a woman $50,000 because she claimed that a cable-car accident had caused her to become a nymphomaniac! Perhaps that's why I noticed an embarrassment of middle-aged women pushing embarrassed middle-aged men onto the cable-cars whilst saying that hanging on to the outside was a bit of a laugh.

Back in 1889, Rudyard Kipling visited San Francisco and wrote about how the cable cars glided to all points of the compass, made San Francisco dead level and, bar passing a building that hummed with machinery, showed no visible agency for their flight. He gave up asking questions, adding that if it pleased Providence to make a car run up and down a slit in the ground for many miles, why should he, for the sake of tuppence-halfpenny, seek reasons of the miracle.

Why indeed?

Apart from the entertainment to be enjoyed from hanging on to the outside of the cable-car as it perilously tips to go down Hyde, or when your legs get a slapping from the yellow plastic posts that are attached to the road (especially on Powell Street), you have the opportunity to meet a variety a characters as well: and I don't mean just the conductors.

I can recall one fine morning – again, not that that really narrows it down, as almost every morning was fine – when taking the Powell-Hyde cable-car down to Fisherman's Wharf, I was unfortunate enough to overhear the following conversation. Perhaps I should first describe the participants, as that may give an indication of why my ears paid special attention.

On my left was a man, probably in his forties, who had chosen to face the day wearing a baseball cap, garish calf-length trousers, white socks and sandals. For that alone he should have been asked to stay indoors. But, as if to compound the travesty of

226

his appearance, he was also sporting a stomach that would have been more at home on a lady within twenty minutes of giving birth to sextuplets. The man then decided, through the act of speaking, to remove any lingering doubts amongst his fellow travellers that he was someone to be spurned.

"Does this cable-car go all the way to Fisherman's Wharf?" he asked.

"Sure," answered the conductor; a pleasantly spoken man of African origin, who had a smile as wide as the Bay Bridge.

"Are there shops down there?"

"Sure." The smile was still as wide

"Can you get food there?"

"Sure." Smile still there, but some of the elasticity was missing.

"Burgers and fries?"

"Uh-huh." 'Fixed' would now be an apt description of said smile.

"And beer?"

No verbal reply this time; just an incredulous nod, and the smile having sagged into obscurity.

"Great."

The sense of shame coming from his fellow countrymen was palpable: and believe you me, it takes quite a bit to discomfit the inhabitants of San Francisco. I almost felt ashamed myself. This canker was going down to one of the best-known parts of the City, and all he was interested in was whether or not he would be able to shovel comestibles down his throat. I do not think I was alone in hoping that some of it was going to get stuck therein.

Then, while I was enjoying the return ride, someone asked how to get to China Town.

"Get off at the next stop," came the reply. "Then keep going that-away until the signs don't make no sense."

But, as jovial as most of the cable-car operators were, I saw one or two that might have learned their particular brand of

227

bonhomie from a Great White. Cheery was not the first adjective that sprang to mind; and woe betide anyone who pulled the cord in order to request that the cable-car paused at the next stop. That was a major no-no.

However, I think that my favourite, spoken by a conductor on the Powell-Mason cable-car route, was ...

"Siddown," he blurted at some unfortunate who had the temerity to stand up between stops. "Why you in such a hurry anyway. You're ahn vacation, right? I'll tell ya when to geddoff."

Yes indeed, many a happy hour I was to spend travelling on the cable-cars until, as Kipling put it, they could go no further. Then I would disembark and stand, experiencing a mixture of bewilderment and amusement, while I watched the driver (or grip-man as they are called) and the conductor get out and push the cable-car on a turntable until it faced the other way – ready to make the return journey. The cable-cars on the California Street were excused this procedure, as they seemed capable of travelling in either direction.

Were such journeys expensive? Surely more so than the tuppence-halfpenny back in 1889? Not really. Well, possibly. It seemed that it cost two dollars to make one trip, going up to six dollars for an all-day pass. But it was possible to purchase something called a 'Fast Pass', and, for $35 dollars, you were allowed unlimited travel on all forms of public transport (except one, I think, but I can't remember which) for a whole month. So, all you have to do is make three cable-car trips a day for six days and you're in profit: and you got three days grace at the end of the month on the cable-cars as well!

I've just noticed something – when did the second vertical line in the dollar symbol disappear? Something to do with the two pillars outside the temple of Solomon wasn't it? Ah well.

<u>The joys of eating out.</u>

As an Englishman who is used to fairly basic eating requirements, I have to say that I found many aspects of eating out in the City a tad on the daunting side.

My first encounter with a situation that showed up my limitations was in a small eatery that proclaimed it was a purveyor of a certain style of cuisine, and went by the name of 'Soul Food'.

I wasn't entirely sure if that meant that the food was good for one's character, got served with a finger-clicking blues sauce, or that the proprietor simply didn't know the difference between a trout and a trumpet.

Gabriella and I went in and were met, in an otherwise empty restaurant, by an oldish woman of African origin; who had a scarf on her head, a red and white pinafore that covered a very creased tracksuit top, a yellow skirt, rather saggy blue ankle-socks, and a pair of slippers. My first instinct was to run. Fast. Towards the door. But before I could move a muscle, she spoke.

"Whad y'all want? Huh?"

I felt so much better.

"Breakfast. Please." I tentatively replied.

"Kay. Take a seat."

"At any table in particular?"

"Where y'all like."

"Is anywhere more convenient for you?" I asked, trying to seem considerate, so that she wouldn't turn nasty.

"You wanna sit in the kitchen? That's real convenient."

"I ... that is ... we can if -"

The rest of my reply was cut short by a rather sharp blow to the front of my right tibia, from the rather sharp end of Gabriella's right shoe.

"Listen, it don't make no di'frence to me, y'hear. Ah's got tables out dair."

"No. Thank you," said Gabriella smiling. "We'll have one over here."

"Please y'self. Ah'll be long shortly."

Gabriella and I knew that as it was a Sunday morning, alternatives in that part of town were going to be few and far between and, after a little bit of deliberation, soon decided on one of the tables near the windows in the next room along. Chosen because it was in the sunlight, because it felt airy, and because it was near one of the doors. Just in case. One never knows.

A few minutes later, the font of etiquette returned.

"What j'all sit in her fo? Huh? Can't d'jew git no foidah away? Huh?"

"I'm sure we could if we - " Another sharp blow arrived.

"Whad j'all eatin' anyhow?"

"Can we have a menu, please?" Gabriella asked. I would have, but I felt sure that our waitress might well have destroyed my head by breathing fire at me had I done so.

"A whert?"

"A menu."

"Tsk ... jeez ..." and, with what sounded like a snarl, the lady left again. "Here," she said, when she returned, throwing a couple of heavily stained pieces of laminated cardboard onto the table.

"Thank you," Gabriella replied, seeming to all the world as if the attitude adopted by the charming lady with the interesting dress sense was normal.

"So? What d'y'all havin anyhows?"

"I think I might need a moment or two to peruse your list of fares," I said, anxious to deflect some of the toxins away from Gabriella.

"Huh?"

"Can you recommend anything?" Gabriella quietly asked, as if knowing that an elaborate request from me might provoke trouble.

"Just what's dair. Iz'all good."

"Okay. Then I think we'll have two eggs on toast, over easy, with hash browns. Twice. Please."

"Right. You want summin a'drink?"

"Coffee, please."

"Juice?"

"Orange, thank you."

"Be right back."

The food arrived in about five minutes, so there was no cause for complaint on that score, and our gracious attendant seemed happy as well: and then I spoke.

"Um ... I wonder if we might have some cutlery ... please."

"You want silverware?"

"Stainless steel will do, thank you."

"Whert?"

"Stainless steel cutlery will be fine. Thank you."

"Cut-ler-ree? Whert in hail's name is thayt?"

"A, er, knife and fork." I then made a little action with my hands to show what I would use them for, and I received another stabbing pain in my shinbone.

"Ah knows what a friggin' knife and foke is. So what in hell's you talkin' 'bout cut-ler-ree fo-waa? Huh?"

"Cutlery. From the English word ... 'Cutler' ... someone who makes, repairs, or deals in knives and cutting implements."

"Well, we ain't got nunner dat. So, you want silverware or what?"

"Please. Thank you ... so much."

It was probably just as well that neither Gabriella nor I took sugar.

My second food-serving encounter was in a very nice sandwich bar that went by the name of Lee's.

My intention had been to slip in and get myself a sandwich that I could take with me to eat – al fresco, so to speak – in the Yerba Buena gardens. A simple enough notion: a bacon sandwich; no real problems. Maybe a dash of mustard: you know the sort of thing. Well, it seems that the lady of Oriental persuasion behind the counter did not. The conversation went something along the lines of ...

"Next."

"Oh... yes... Hello. Um, could I have a bacon sandwich, please?"

"What kinda bread?"

"White. Thank you."

"Huh?"

"White. Please."

"What kinda white?"

"What kind of white? I ... er ... what kind of white do you have?"

"We got 5 grain, 9 grain, 12 grain, wholegrain, rye, wheat, pumpernickel, potato poppyseed, honey oat and honey corn."

It was then that my mouth fell open slightly, and I began to emit a rather peculiar gargling sound – caused, so I believe, by my tongue falling backwards into my throat and then flapping up and down.

"Sir?"

I managed to clear the obstruction, and then pointed at the loaf that was closest.

"Sourdough?"

I have to say that I didn't like her implication, but I nodded all the same.

"You want 'cado with it?"

I nodded again, still having no idea what she was talking about; but now acutely aware of some rather irritated, and incredulous, looks from several people in the queue behind me.

"Mayorstard?"

I nodded again, still absolutely clueless.

"Tomaydoe?"

Another nod.

"Pickle?"

Yet another.

The young lady then, with as swift a display of legerdemain as I can ever recall witnessing, had the sandwich wrapped, cut in two, wrapped again and handed to me. I managed a faint 'thank you' before shuffling off to pay.

It was only when I reached the park that I found out what it was I had purchased; and how damn near impossible it was going to be to take a bite without first standing on it. It was enormous: and as for the contents ...

True, I had got the bacon I wanted ...lots of it ... but, unfortunately, it was all cooked to a frazzle. There was also a lot of mushy green stuff that, after a few minutes consideration, I worked out to be avocado: I couldn't recall asking for that, but as I am not allergic to it, I pressed ahead. There was some lettuce, slices of tomato, and an awful lot of white sauce that tasted like nothing I had tried before, that was intent on covering my clothes every time I bit into the sandwich. There were also several long slices of what looked like gherkin; but absolutely no sign of the pickle I distinctly remembered agreeing to have. Still, I judiciously took the attitude that having three things I didn't ask for somewhat compensated for being short of one that I did.

You will be pleased to know, I'm sure, that the 'sandwich' eventually found its way into the confines of my stomach; and, despite causing me to look as if the thing had exploded at some stage, wasn't half bad.

As for the Yerba Buena gardens - it really is a splendid place for enjoying one's lunch: and, if the number of people there

233

was any indication, it was a popular place for consuming the occasional plate of provender. Soft grass, a whispering waterfall – courtesy of M. Luther King's memory no less – and, on that particular day, a rather enthusiastic five-piece band. I say 'enthusiastic', but I really mean 'loud'. Nobody else seemed too concerned about the volume, so perhaps I was sitting at the exact spot where the directional sound from the loudspeakers converged. Or maybe the others thought that, compared to the normal City noises, it was fairly quiet.

I then went inside what is known as the Metreon Centre to get myself a coffee: and what a kafuffle that was. Once again, I am quite sure the fault lay entirely with yours truly; but all the same. Why can't they have a section of the counter for people like me who just want a cup of coffee? Instant, with a dash of milk or cream: nothing fancy: just a choice of two types of coffee – black or white.

But no, that would be far too easy: it's much more fun to have eighty-seven different types of coffee. On top of which, all the beans come as either hand or machine-picked, fine or coarse-ground, fresh or freeze-dried; and can be served with full-fat, half-and-half, low-fat, 1%, 2%, sem-eye-skimmed, and half a dozen other types of milk that made no sense at all and had probably never been anywhere near a cow.

Is it any wonder that a chap feels a bit confused?

But what a place that Metreon Centre turned out to be. I don't know about you, but I'm a bit of a sucker for gadgets. Show me an electrical device for doing something and I will, more often than not, be inclined to go and purchase one. Actually, that's not strictly true. I think it used to be so in my halcyon days, but with age comes a dash of wisdom: or at least that is what's meant to happen. Not always the case, I realise, but there we are. Anyway, I tend to ponder awhile these days, weighing up the pros and cons, before deciding that my life might not necessarily be enhanced as per all the advertising blarney.

I did think about purchasing one of those enormous television sets that seem to be several yards wide and takes up one of the walls in your lounge. But then, perchance, I noticed – whilst involved in a touch of said pondering and viewing the same broadcast on adjacent sets – that the wide-screen televisions might show a bit more at the edges, but they do seem to cut off a bit from the top and bottom. And if the programme isn't being broadcast in the 'wide-screen' format, it does have a tendency to make everyone look as if they have been at the sweet trolley a bit too often.

Then we have the sound systems that require several speakers - sometimes upwards of four of the blessed things - to be strategically located around the room. Why? It seems to me that most – if not all – of the action takes place within the confines of the television set and, surely, that is from where most – if not all – of the sound should come. Why would I want to look at the 'star of the show' who is performing in one corner of my lounge, and yet be able to hear his voice coming from another corner – possibly even from behind the curtains? It would seem that everyone on the television has taken up the art of voice throwing. All very confusing.

Anyway, if you have a big television you tend to sit further away from it, not wanting to strain the eyeballs and suchlike; so why buy one? Twenty feet away from a forty-inch screen is pretty much the same as ten feet away from a twenty-inch screen. Isn't it? And how many people have enough room in their lounges to be able to put twenty feet between them and the television in the first place?

But in the Centre they had enormous televisions for sale. Absolutely huge they were. So big, in fact, that to watch the screen you had to keep moving your head from side to side: rather like watching a tennis match! Absolutely exhausting, and, as if another reason not to buy one was needed, it also made me feel a bit nauseous.

Next I came across the 'TV Games' area. What a place, and what an array of awfully complicated-looking games they had therein. I can remember my father bringing back a television game – in the days when colour television sets were pretty thin on the ground – that consisted of having to control paddles that went up and down on either side of the screen, and hit a white dot that went across from one side of the screen to the other. I can't remember if it was meant to be tennis or squash, but the object of the game was to use the paddles to 'bat' the dot back and forth across the screen. Mind-numbingly boring by present-day standards, but back then? ... Absolutely fantastic.

Rather like the old computers that stored information on cassette tape. Or how about those ones that used reels – about the size of a dustbin lid – and had to be housed in a room with a constantly maintained temperature? Massive and slow beyond belief when compared with the zillions of megahertz used these days: but magical in their day.

Anyway, back to the TV games. Or are they called 'Arcade Games'? I once had a go at playing something called 'Tombraider', which worked on a console called a 'Playstation'. My previous foray into this world of wizardry had been on a contraption called a SEGA Megadrive and, I seem to recall, featured a game or two that starred a hedgehog. Yes, I was probably a bit on the grown-up side to have been playing with such things; but it was great fun all the same. Not that I admitted as such to anyone I knew! Then I was introduced to a game that

236

went by the title of 'Flashback'. Well, that took things onto another level altogether. Sore thumbs all round.

But back to 'Tombraider'. I had managed to acquire something known as a 'Walkthrough' that, essentially, is a detailed list of how to get through the various levels, picking up the secrets and what have you on the way. My sister's son took no time in labelling me a cheat; which, I suppose, in a way I was. But, in my defence, if I had not acquired said 'Walkthrough', the main character – Lara Croft, splendid lady – would probably have not got much further into the adventure than finding a place to park her car.

I am well aware that there are people who can whiz through all the levels in less time than it takes me to find out where to insert the memory card; and I am also well aware that those same people spend a lot of their waking hours improving their techniques and getting to grip with all the new games as they are released. I, however, have never felt that my days would be enhanced, even slightly, by knowing which of the newer consoles offered the best polygons and animations, or allowed one to rip one's own music to the hard disk. On top of which, I like to think I have a life.

Anyway, most of the modern techno-game stuff is way, way above the Phalarope parietal regions, I don't mind admitting. Like rather a lot of the gadgets about these days, by the time I begin to get the old grey matter round it, the blighters who produce it have gone and brought out the 'super-duper' version. Small wonder that a fellow can get a complex.

So there I was, doing a 'walkthrough' of my own, looking at all the people – of all ages – who were fixed in front of screens and game consoles; finger-flicking, twisting their torsos in time with the action, and with expressions that showed the sort of concentration that one would normally expect to see on an active member of a bomb disposal team. Mind you, some of the players were having to negotiate manoeuvres that, if not carried out properly, could well have blown up an entire continent.

237

There were all sorts of activities: virtual ten-pin bowling, virtual water and snow skiing, virtual driving, and virtual cities. Rather obviates the need to ever leave one's abode. Extraordinary state of affairs. There was even a – I'm not sure what to call it: maybe 'contraption' best suits – contraption that required you to put on a pair of boxing gloves and, by means of sensors and circuitry beyond any range of comprehension that I might have to describe it, 'fight' with a rather aggressive-looking virtual opponent. Not really my cup of tea, I have to say. No, give me a game of chess anytime.

But, as if to stress the point that technology moves faster than most people can keep up, the sophistication of present-day games is mind-boggling. I would love to run through some of the advances for you, but I'm afraid that even the vocabulary needed is several rungs on the ladder above the one where my cerebellum is currently residing. Maybe another time.

I get to meet Tom and Paul.

At the start of my fourth week, Gabriella suggested that, in order to experience a bit more of the San Francisco flavour, I might like to meet a couple of her friends.

"I would be delighted," I said, ever keen to broaden my mind.

"I've booked a table at an Italian restaurant. Is that okay?"

Have I mentioned my dislike of Garlic? I think it only fair to point out that as well as associating the aroma with oily continental types, I have an unfortunate ability to continue tasting said ampoule d'odeur for days, if not weeks, afterwards. I am unable to comment on my own resultant fetor oris, but if it is merely half as unpleasant as that belonging to others who have had the desire to get themselves outside the wretched stuff, then my breath could successfully be used to remove wallpaper.

However, despite preferring to indulge in a round of Chinese cuisine, I merely smiled and shrugged my shoulders.

As I mentioned earlier, I'm not sure if it is an hereditary trait in the Phalarope lineage to go all gooey when faced with a beautiful woman; but it is something that seems to afflict me from time to time. Put me face to face with ne'er-do-wells intent on relieving me of funds, and I will maintain a bearing that Richard Coeur de Lion would have been proud to call his own. But put me up against someone of the female persuasion who happens to own a phizog that could well launch an aircraft carrier and, mysteriously, the calcium content of my vertebrae seems to vanish.

"Oh, by the way" the vision of loveliness continued, "Tom and Paul are both gay."

"Oh. Ah."

"Are you all right with that?"

"Hmm?"

"Are you okay, William? You seem to have gone a bit pale."

I have to admit to rather hoping that my evening with Ron would have been my last close encounter with gentleman whose inclinations inclined the other way to my own. Perhaps Gabriella noticed a little quiver in my top lip.

"William?"

"Yes."

"Are you sure you're okay?"

"Yes, thank you. I'm fine."

I have no arguable explanation for the discomfort that I feel when thinking about matters of a homosexual nature, or those who indulge in same, but the whole thing does make me feel decidedly uneasy. However, stoic that I am, I hauled my 'visage courageux' out of the case (I nearly said out of the closet — ha!) and stuck it on. I wasn't sure if Gabriella was all that convinced.

And so, when eight o'clock that evening rolled around, I was to be found sitting at a rather small table, in a rather crowded Italian restaurant, in a rather fashionable part of San Francisco. I don't know about you, but I never feel relaxed in crowded restaurants that have small tables: especially if the restaurant is frequented by the 'in' crowd. I always feel trapped, and I hate the way the waiters hang around in the obsequious manner that they tend to adopt. If I want extra pepper, I'll reach for it; if I want more wine, I am more than capable of pouring it from a bottle into my glass: and, no, the lady doesn't want a rose – or any other over-priced blossom either - so buzz off.

I am more than happy to dip into my accounts to procure blooms for a charmante when I wish to faire l'amant, as they say in the better parts of France; but I would rather be hanged than part with a bit of the old Librae, Solidi, Denarii in exchange for something the maître d'hotel probably purloined from a passing cortège.

Any further contemplation was interrupted when I became aware of a slight contretemps taking place near the entrance, and my attention was drawn towards two gentlemen – one of a slightly effeminate Chinese bearing, and the other more closely resembling a bison that had decided to shave its head – who were indulging in rather a lot of arm-waving with the doorman and shouting in a dialect that I didn't recognise.

I was about to make a comment about how such people really ought not to be allowed into eateries when Gabriella stood up, waved at the two men, and then informed me that her friends had arrived.

I have a feeling that the expression on my face must have mirrored that of the man who had just been told that his wife was leaving him for the milkman, that she was taking the children with her, and that he wasn't to worry as they weren't his anyway. I would like to think that said expression had begun to fade before Tom and Paul reached our table.

Now, I must point out that I use the term 'table' loosely, as I have seen Olympic athletes throw discuses with a greater diameter. Al Oerter, for one, would have done it far more justice than the use to which it was currently being put. Possibly a cooper who specialised in making miniature barrels might have put in an offer for it. For my own part, I like a table to look and behave like a table, as I rather object to noticing the butter from my side plate has disappeared and then finding it stuck to the elbow of the person sitting next to me. There should be a minimum size of table that is rigorously enforced by the Health and Safety Gestapo - instead of wasting their time (and the tax payers' money) by, for instance, stopping primary schools holding sack races. Anyway.

Gabriella exchanged air-kisses with both of the men, before the effeminate Chinese one extended a very slender arm in my direction saying, "Well hello ... you must be William. I'm Paul." I shook the hand that was situated at the end of the aforementioned arm. "And this is Tom."

I have a feeling that I may have shied away slightly, as an arm the size of my leg suddenly appeared from beneath a massive black fur coat and headed in my direction. Taking a moment to acknowledge the yelp of indignation from the diner behind me after I had caused him to flick consommé at the rather odd-looking lady sitting in front of him, I shook the hand sticking out from Tom's sleeve – for what seemed like half my life – before being allowed to have it back and check to see if I still had all my fingers.

241

Any further protestations from the aforementioned diner were swiftly shelved as soon as he had spotted the reason for my involuntary movement.

Then we all sat down; as close to the table as it was possible without interlocking our legs. Whilst the prospect of doing so with Gabriella certainly held a great deal of appeal, I rather felt that contact with either of the gentlemen's lower limbs was about as appealing as answering a personal advertisement in the 'Bay Times'.

I had just about managed to get my autonomic nervous system to function without drawing attention to itself when one of the ubiquitous serving staff approached our table and asked if we would like anything to drink. A reasonable enough gesture, and meant with all the good intentions imaginable, I would have thought: and I am quite sure that a response agreeable to all would have been achieved had Tom not felt compelled to answer on our behalf.

Before I describe how the unfortunate cameriere fainted and collapsed onto what little floor space there was, perhaps I should bring to your attention a couple of rather salient facts.

Firstly, Tom was not what could, even by stretching one's imagination to near breaking point, be described as a 'pretty boy'. In fact, his resemblance to one of the large mammals that historians have described as roaming the prairies in appreciable numbers is so near the mark that wildlife documentary makers have, so I believe, been known to camp for several days in the vicinity of his apartment in the hope of catching a glimpse.

Secondly, and probably more importantly, is the fact that Tom is stone deaf. Although quite an accomplished lip-reader, and the owner of two rather snazzy hearing aids, his aural acuity is not up there amongst the best. Also, rather like some of the people who have been deaf since a young age, he is not always able to accurately judge the intonation or volume of his own speech.

The net result is that what should have been "Not just at the moment, thank you," spoken in a volume sufficient not to be heard from a distance of more than four feet, actually came out as "Bow ustata moo-mentankou," in a volume sufficient to blow out all the candles on an adjacent table. And, thus, cause the waiter to turn white, clutch his tie, and then lie down on the floor.

Tom, to his credit, did feel somewhat responsible and, before anybody had time to stop him, decided to stand up and bellow across the room for some assistance. At least that's what I presume was his intention. Unfortunately, Tom adopted the same degree of volume and enunciation control as before and, consequently, gave the other diners the impression that some kind of fire-drill had been initiated and that they should leave the premises in as quick and as orderly a fashion as they could.

The other diners got the 'quick' part right, but the 'orderly' segment of the arrangement, alas, fell by the wayside somewhat. Food and drink were spilled, and some of the tables were knocked over as pandemonium broke out. It was fully twenty minutes before the staff was able to reassure all the patrons that it was safe to return.

All the patrons, that is, apart from those who had been seated at our table. For some reason, the proprietors were anxious to see the back of us. The silver lining of all the excitement was I didn't have to go anywhere near garlic.

"Well, I just hope you're satisfied with all of that," Paul said to Tom, as the four of us congregated under a streetlamp outside.

"Huh?"

"I said I hope you're ... Oh, what's the use?"

"Eh?"

"I am so sorry, William. I guess you were really looking forward to your meal."

"Fret ye not, Paul. I'm sure we'll find somewhere else."

"But it's such a shame that the evening has been spoilt."

"Don't worry about it. As I said, I'm -"

"Wha?" asked Tom, still many decibels above a sufficiency.

"I wasn't talking to you," snapped Paul. "And I'm quite sure that William doesn't want to hear your excuses."

"Wha ah ooh aying?"

At that, Paul crossed his arms, turned his head to one side, and pursed his lips so tightly that I thought the skin on his chin was going to split. "You are really gonna get it when we get back to the apartment," he then snapped at Tom.

"Pomises ... pomises," Tom replied, completely missing the point.

"Oh ... you ..."

"I'm gonna get me a big cake," Tom then added, before stomping off like a petulant grizzly bear.

"From where?" Paul shrieked, as he pattered after him.

"Um air."

The rest of the discourse faded as the two of them rounded the corner and disappeared into the night. I looked at Gabriella, shrugged my shoulders and smiled. She looked back, smiled and shrugged her shoulders.

"Chinese?" she asked.

"Marvellous."

Open Studio Day.

October, so it transpired, is a month in which quite a few events are scheduled to take place in the City; and one of those events takes place over four weekends, and goes by the name of 'Open Studios'. I have already touched upon my limited knowledge – and even less appreciation - of what is often referred

244

to as Modern Art; so I was a little less than enthusiastic when Gabriella suggested that it might be fun if we partook.

"Partook of what?" I gingerly enquired.

"We go and see some of the studios."

"*Some* of them! How many are there?"

"Maybe upwards of one hundred artists."

"A hundred! But that's ... it's ..."

"A lot. I know. But we don't have to see them all."

"I should jolly well – Oh, that's a shame."

So, with my sense of foreboding a little reduced – not by much, I have to say, but enough to stop me from shaking – we made arrangements to go and have a squiz at some of the studios in the locale.

I am, I most readily admit, a bit on the bereft side of things when it comes to understanding objets d'art that are not instantly recognisable as what they are meant to be. A painting of a bowl of fruit leaves me with little to occupy the grey matter apart from how nice the fruit looks. I do not recognise it as a harvest concatenation depicting the frailty of life: I simply see a bowl of fruit.

Similarly, put me in front of a half-made bed and all I see is a half-made bed. My mind does not go wandering down avenues lined with thoughts of man's inhumanity or his pointless search for immortality. My mind, along with the rest of my being, sees, as I said, a half-made bed; and a pointless reason for handing over vast sums of lucre for something that most people own and can see every day of the week. Especially if they share my notion that a bed needs to be aired on a daily basis, and that the duration of said airing exactly coincides with the hours between rising and retiring. Nature knows best, I always say.

As for a pile of bricks, half a cow, or a collection of broken plates? Well, they, likewise, do nothing for me at all; other than make me feel as though I must have missed a good party, and wish that I had an agent who was capable of getting people to part with fistfuls of their hard-earned in exchange for something that I would be embarrassed to leave out for the bin-men. Anyway, off we went.

Our first stop was a studio in North Beach, and the proprietor welcomed us both as we entered. The room was about thirty feet by twenty and had a selection of freestanding works dotted about the place. It seemed that the tragedy at the World Trade Centre had been an inspiration, of sorts, for the artist who had made (or would the term 'assembled' be more accurate?) several works that looked as though they may well have been found amongst all the rubble.

Now, apart from having no idea what they were, I would have had no idea where to put them had I been foolish enough to purchase one. I mean, where do you put something that looks like part of a garden trellis (apart from with the rest of the trellis, I suppose) that had been burned in one corner and had several bits of cloth hanging from another? Certainly nowhere near the back door, I should imagine, in case it was put outside along with the rest of the rubbish.

Our second port of call was a very small apartment in which the owner/painter had hung many of his unframed works. Having seen them, I think it would have been a better idea to have hung the painter instead. Okay, fair enough, he was brave enough to have invited people – complete strangers, no less – into his home in order for them to look at his work; and – fair enough – they didn't all look as though a six-year old had been involved; and – even more of the validation – my artistic skills have never been much in advance of those shown by an irascible mongoose: but all the same.

Although I feel obliged, by way of mitigation, to say that I did do pottery while I was at school. Further, with a small accompaniment of self-blown trumpetry, I once got round to making a nude - of the female persuasion I hasten to add – in clay.

Now, allowing for the fact that I was only about thirteen years old, and had never seen a nude female (the school seemed

246

very reluctant to allow such an addition to the class, although I'm sure that all the boys – and the teacher as well, I expect – would have warmly welcomed her), I was probably a tad under-informed of the general anatomical arrangements. However, possibly as a result of a mixture of bravado and wishful thinking, I felt equipped to tackle the task. Regrettably, although well intentioned, I was somewhat short of hands-on experience (if you'll pardon the pun) and had no real concept of size.

The net result was a lady with two (well, at least I got the number right) rather large, and extremely well-appointed (or do I just mean pointed) breasts that bore little relation to normal human mammary arrangements, but rather a lot to the object often spotted on top of the head of a Pierrot: without the pom-pom, that is. Although I have since seen some answering that description at a certain club in - Enough already!

As a further blow to my self-esteem, the legs weren't much good either. No matter how hard I tried, they always ended up looking like two strips of spaghetti (devoid of all known points of articulation) or two beer-bottles. In the end, and after much shedding of sweat, I decided that – for the sake of my sanity (and that of the plethora of schoolboys who had gathered around and were as much in the dark as I was, regarding the nuances of the female form) I ought to turn the lady into a mermaid. The end result, even if I have to say so myself, was rather good. She still had bosoms that could poke out your eye, mind you; but of such are the dreams of thirteen-year old boys made.

Our third port of call was an altogether more professional affair: and I don't just mean that the items on display were more expensive – although they were. No, even to a complete novice like me, it was apparent that the wares on show were from a different league. Unfortunately, I lost any understanding of what was going on from the moment I read that the 'contrapposto sense of balance and strong chiaroscuro lighting of the portraits revealed the artist's classical training in Rome'.

I also lost a slight amount of willingness to find out any more when the artist explained that her portraits 'reflected the texture and colour that the sitter brought to their family and community, and that they honoured the unique life experience that was etched into each sitter's features'.

There was I thinking that a portrait was meant to look like the sitter – or at least a flattering aspect of them. Unless, as with a certain Oliver Cromwell, you want a 'warts and all' production. Before all you aficionados leap in with quotes of 'character and composure', I have already worked out that the payer of the piper calls the tune; so the payer of the painter will, as so often happens, offer advice on the size of the nose, the close proximity of the eyes, and the abundance of the hair.

But how does one reflect the texture that the sitter brought to the community? How does one bring texture to the community in the first place? Are we discussing someone who renders the outside walls of their house with Hessian? What if the sitter is someone who makes a living entering people's houses by way of an open window, and then removing items of value? Beats me. A flaw in my education I expect.

I think that my apathy was further compounded when I was informed that the sitter would be told to bring along four of their favourite CDs to lend to the artist until the work was finished. Apparently they are used as personal input from the sitter during the long completion process of the portrait. Yes, of course they are.

But, as I have intimated - actually I think I did more than merely intimate - I am not the person to phone when you need advice on a work of art. I do, however, have one or two works of art hanging on the walls at my home. Nothing outlandish – the works, not the walls: although, come to think of it, the walls are two feet thick; and without a cavity in the middle – but they do rest easily on the old retinas. As do the walls; and they were not built in the manner that modern-day building regulatory officials would smile upon: but the building is still standing after nearly one hundred and fifty years. I wonder who knows best? Quod Erat Demonstrandum!

Speaking of building, a very good friend of mine once decided to build a snooker room; actually it was more of a snooker bungalow – about thirty-six feet by twenty. His reasoning was that he wanted enough room to be able to comfortably use a cue from all angles (that meant, with a six by twelve table, he would need a room of twenty-four feet by eighteen for starters), and he thought that it might be rather a good idea to have some comfortable chairs at one end so that people could watch. Then he decided that a bit more room - for a bar and piano - would round it off nicely: and so it did: and, may I say, many a splendid evening was enjoyed there.

He – a japester by the name of Jonathon Clewless – did have one or two 'house rules', as he liked to call them, that had to be adhered to by those wishing to use his table. Amongst the things on the list of absolute No-Nos, were people under five and a half feet tall (regardless of whether they were wearing high-heels or not ... in fact, *especially* if they were wearing high-heels), the use of blue chalk, people with less (or more) than the prescribed number of hands and eyes, fat people, people whose age exceeded their IQ, people with squints, people who smoked, and (most important of all) people who were any good at the game.

Fortunately, I'm pleased to say, I fell well within the compass of all those criteria and, as I said, Jonathon and I spent many a happy evening playing snooker. Well, I say 'playing' snooker, but it was more like moving the balls around the baize until one of them fell into a pocket. Although I seem to recall our fastest time for a frame was just under one hour and ten minutes. Not bad, eh?

And that happy idyll would have continued for many a year, had it not been for the imprudent – and frequent - imbibing of alcohol undertaken by his then wife. Poor old Jonathon. That wretched woman made his life a blessed misery for years, and then divorced him; and was last seen heading towards their joint bank account with a large wheelbarrow and shovel. She took away just about all he had: including the children. Mind you, if truth be told, Jonathon was rather pleased about that part, as the issue of their joint loins wasn't the sort of thing you would want inflicted on you.

Don't get me wrong, I have nothing against children. Well, not so long as they belong to other people, never spend a night under my roof, and I don't have to communicate with them in any way. My sister's progeny being a prime case in point. I think that I may have referred to them earlier in this prose ... I am just pausing while I try and think of their names ... oh yes, Tarquin and Mirabella. Ghastly things; practically brings me out in hives just thinking about them.

Once again, on the grounds of fair play and all that, I would like to point out that I would fully support – male or female - the aggrieved party in the disintegration of any connubial alliance that didn't last the distance. But I do wish to express my displeasure at seeing so many of my fellow hombres being dumped on from so great a height by a legal system that thinks it just dandy to let the woman take whatever – and even much more than - she thinks fit. Yes, I do agree that in the past things were a bit on the heavy side for women; but letting the pendulum swing too far the other way does not bring about restitution, or engender future amicable settlements. On the contrary: and, as usual, the only people who benefit are the lawyers; whose motto, I feel sure, is 'Creare Odium' – and also to charge an arm and a leg in the process.

A rather ghastly thought has just occurred to me: and it came as a bit of a shock I can tell you. Firstly, because I am not prone to bursts of spontaneous cerebral activity; and secondly, because of the subject matter. What if Sis and her spouse were to peg it?

Upsetting to a certain degree, I've no doubt: but what about their progeny? Where would they go? Rather a worry, that. And, as the basis of my cause for concern, what if my sibling has decided to play a final joke on younger brother and made some sort of bequest regarding the future accommodation of her brood? I must remember to send her some literature on healthy living and other aids to longevity.

I seem to have strayed again. Where was I? Oh yes, works of art at my cottage. I once crossed paths with a fellow – Jim, I think his name was – who had a fantastic talent in the art department. He possessed a wonderful ability to transpose onto paper whatever he saw in front of him; and whether in the form of pencil or paint, he could reproduce the image. But his greatest skill – to a humble non-artisan like me, you understand – was the ability to make these images in eggshells. He would take eggshells – mainly from hens' eggs – crush them into small bits, and then stick them onto a piece of stained plywood in such a way that ... Well, whatever it was he was looking at, that was what appeared. Quite extraordinary.

I have three framed works of his – two of peacocks and one of a Samurai warrior about to slay a dragon – and they have pride of place on my walls: and a very good conversation opener they always prove to be. I told Jim that I would be happy to take photographs of his work – au gratis, of course – so that he could construct a type of portfolio, and visit places such as restaurants and offices in order to make some kind of deal whereby if they allowed him to hang them and sell them, he would pass on a percentage of the sale price to the proprietor. Seemed a good idea to me. Last I heard of Jim he was working as a roofer. One thinks of horses and their inclination, or otherwise, to drink water.

I did have a go at painting myself. Not actually painting *myself*, you understand, but doing the painting myself; if you see what I mean. I chose oils as my preferred medium: not because I felt that oils would best allow me to express myself, but because they would best allow me to cover up all the shortcomings in my ability. Then, when all attempts at correction had failed, I could tell people that I was simply experimenting with impressionism.

I once tried painting a beach at night. Not doing the painting at night, but showing what a beach would look like at night: or should I say what a beach *might* look like at night. A moonlit one, that is, or else the canvas would have been introduced to an awful lot of black paint and it could have been misinterpreted as a cellar.

So imagine if you will, a sandy shore, waves gently lapping, no wind to speak of, and the daylight spectrum of visible colours giving way to subtle shades of grey. Rather like the picture on a black and white television. Wonderful concept, I thought, so I sallied forth. I stuck in a couple of palm trees to give it depth, and I thought that a horse or two cantering through the shallow water would add a touch of development.

I decided to have one of the horses appearing from stage right – just the front half of the horse – but try as I might, I couldn't get the horse to look other than something designed by Odysseus (probably without the help of Athena) and left lurking around the entrance to Troy. I very nearly added Sinon to the picture, with the notion that it might help it along! But my desire to stick with the beach scene prevailed over that of wanting to recreate a part of Greek history, and I decided that it would be best to convert the front of said equine into the side of a wooden native hut.

Although the alteration was successfully completed, I felt that some animation was still required; and so I had another go at introducing a horse. This time the plan was to have it a bit further along the beach and moving with all the grace of a Lipizzaner - water splashing around the fetlock area, its tail flowing in the breeze, and so forth. But no, it wasn't to be. Well, not exactly.

I managed, somehow, to get most of it as I had intended: but the head? Not even close, I'm afraid. What was a chap to do? I didn't think I could arrange for another native hut – certainly not that close to the water - so a fresh ruse had to be forthcoming: and, fortunately, it was.

We Phalaropes have been blessed with the ability to delve pretty deeply into the cupboard of inventions when needs arise, and that day was no exception. After a bit of rooting around I found what I was looking for – a palm tree. Not one that was big enough to hide the whole horse – I had a feeling that would have looked a bit odd; although, upon reflection, the tree could well have been extremely close to the easel - but one that was strategically placed to hide just the animal's head. Brilliant, eh?

What is more, it gave me sufficient confidence to attempt another painting; and the next project was a snow scene. This time I decided to have a small church in the background, several leafless trees, boughs heavily laden with snow, clear blue sky, a robin hopping about, and, in the foreground, a small cart of wood being pulled by – yes, you've guessed it – a horse.

"What!" I hear you exclaim. "Didn't you learn from the beach fiasco?"

Well, in a way I did. I learned to try a good deal harder to get the horse's head right: and this time, somehow, I succeeded. Well, also, in a way. The front half of the animal had all the grace and lines of a Derby winner, and looked absolutely splendid. Unfortunately the back half left one in no doubt that the beast could have hauled enough drays to warrant inclusion in the Guinness Book of Records. It was a formidable rear end, and no mistake. Well, that's not quite true. There was a mistake, and that was not only having the two halves in the same picture, but also having them joined together. And, to add further to my faux pas, I had painted the horse so that it was approaching the viewer – rather than going away – and I was, therefore, unable to blame the appearance of the animal on some trick of parallax. Perhaps I should have heeded the advice a friend once gave me that if at first you don't succeed, try something else: but not to use the maxim with parachuting.

You will be unsurprised to hear that I didn't give up the day job.

I meet an Opinion Pollster.

It was another pleasant afternoon, and I was sauntering down the last block or two of Powell Street – towards Market – when I was approached by a lady who was clasping a clipboard and had a look in her eyes that spoke of a determination that far exceeded anything I could have adequately countered. I thought a couple of swift side-steps would help me escape the ambush; but to my right was a mendicant who might well have sunk his teeth into my leg had I tried to pass without slipping a couple of notes into his polystyrene cup, and to my left there was parked one of the many itinerant 'stretch limos' that have made San Francisco their home. I smiled and accepted my fate.

"Sir, can you spare a few minutes?"

"Apparently."

"Great. I wonder if I could just get you to answer some questions?"

The paradox of, at last, finding somebody who wanted to know my opinion and, simultaneously, finding that I wanted to avoid her, wasn't lost on me. "Fire away, old thing," I said.

"Sir?"

"I'm all yours."

"Huh?"

"What?"

"Eh?"

I had a feeling that it was going to be up to yours truly to put an end to the limited discourse before one of us went a funny colour and swapped the state of California for that of Catatonia. "Do you have something to ask me?" I said.

"Why, yes I do."

The lady then passed me a sheet of paper on which was a string of questions and, alongside each, were three small boxes into one of which – depending on whether I decided mostly yes, maybe, or mostly no – I could place an 'X'. It was about this time that her surprisingly ample bosom made its first appearance, and I have to admit that my concentration was somewhat distracted thereafter.

Now, before any of you ardent feminists start buzzing me with accusations of being a sexist (or whatever other deprecating terms leap to the forefront of your no-doubt extensive vocabulary), I have to hold up both hands and admit that I do seem to be easily distracted by the female chestal area. Not that size has ever been the overriding factor, but when the aforementioned area is large enough on which to comfortably balance a tray of drinks then – parce que je suis seulement un homme – one's gaze does have a tendency to home in somewhat.

I think I should endeavour to make perfectly clear – especially as I may have mentioned the female thoracic regions on more than one occasion – that I do not have a fixation regarding the items normally contained within a woman's double-fronted undergarment. Well, not an unhealthy one anyway.

As long as one does not start to salivate excessively or have one's eyes fall out of their sockets, I think the occasional discreet glance is well within order. After all, on such yearnings is the procreation of Mankind dependent. On top of which, if so many women feel that men staring at them is demeaning their value as a human being, why on earth do so many women take such trouble to leave their houses with a décolletage to which Rubens would have given a 'two-thumbs-up'?

So, I had a quick glance through to see what the general nature of the questions was, and found that there didn't seem to be one. But three of the questions, however, did catch my eye.

1) Are you usually undisturbed by 'noises off' when you are trying to rest?
2) Are your opinions insufficiently important to tell other people?
3) Do you browse through railway timetables for pleasure?

I don't think further comment is necessary. The lady then told me that if I put my address on the form I would be contacted in order to make an appointment for a confidential test analysis. So I did. I wrote that I dwelt on a particular avenue in the Sunset district of the City. I also mentioned that I was very interested in her organisation, that they could turn up any time they wanted, would she tell her agents not to pay any attention if I appeared a little confused when they called, and that they were to press on regardless. In fact, I added, my seeming antipathy is just part of a game I like to play. I do hope that Weiden Spinkbuttock won't be too cross when the San Francisco Something-ology Association comes calling. Actually, that's not quite true: I hope he'll be absolutely furious

What slightly taxed me was being able to keep a straight face when the lady read my form. What slightly worried me was

256

the fact that she didn't turn a hair when she read the name I had put. It seems that America really has cornered the market as far as 'interesting' names are concerned.

Then, with a cheery wave, I respectfully continued on my way. Actually, it wasn't all that respectfully ... I ran for a bus. One of those electric buses that often has to stop for the driver to hop out and reattach the cables to the overhead wires. One of those electric buses where the driver seems not to give a hoot about the wellbeing of his passengers – at least that was the impression I got from the manner in which they accelerate away from the bus-stop, thus causing the passengers to spiral away towards the back of the bus: and then scream to a halt, thus causing the passengers to spiral back to the front again.

All great fun if you're in the mood for it, but a bit trying if you're laden with the weekly groceries. Perhaps there is some kind of contest to see who can put the most passengers into hospital. I'm not sure if such a competition would catch on back home: might be a bit of a wheeze, though.

Speaking of carrying groceries on buses, I had a bit of a shock when I noticed a lady of Oriental origins place her carrier-bags on the floor, and then saw one of the bags start hopping away down the bus. I had no idea that people were able to buy the main course of their evening meal while it was still sucking in God's air and obviously keen on making a break for it. Mind you, that way is probably more salubrious than picking up one of those shrink-wrapped offerings that you find in supermarkets.

Still on the subject of driving, I do not think that if I stayed in San Francisco for a year I would get the hang of the procedure for precedence – drivers or pedestrians – at traffic-light junctions. Quite unfathomable.

The Job Interview debacle.

"Would you like to come to a Job Interview seminar?" Gabriella asked me one day.

"A Job Interview seminar?" I replied.

"Uh-huh."

"And what, pray, is a Job Interview seminar?"

"It's where they train job applicants in techniques for them to use when they go for a job interview."

"Oh. Well ... that is ... I've never really been much of a colloquium connoisseur, you know. Attending lectures is not quite my forte."

"But that's perfect."

"Eh?"

"You could be a guinea pig for them."

"I could?"

"Most of the people there will be practiced applicants: it'll be kinda neat to have someone who is a complete stranger to their procedures."

"Oh."

"Truly."

"Are you quite sure? You don't think I might be an injudicious choice of guinea pig?"

A wave of consideration crossed Gabriella's thoughts. "Good point," she said. "Maybe it's best if we might skip that."

Anyway, like the proverbial lamb, off I was led. I must point out that my experience of seminars has been, to put it mildly, fleeting. I was never much of one for attending things of an official nature: never really much of one for attending a lot of things that involved human beings, if you must know. A bit of a 'non-attender' you might say. "And a jolly good thing too," a lot of people who know me would add. However, we don't really want to hear their views.

But sticking with the saying that 'Les absents ont toujours tort', I have to admit that as a result of me having skipped an entire series of lectures - on something to do with biochemistry I think - I managed to score eleven per cent in the exam. I was asked to present myself before the tutor and explain how this came about.

Fairly easily, I would have thought: but apparently not. It seemed that as the exam was in the nature of a 'multiple choice' format, and as there was a choice of four answers to each question, by virtue of the odds so presented and merely using a pin and closed eyes, I should have scored in the region of twenty-five per cent. Scoring eleven per cent was deemed to be 'extracting the fluids' in a manner that the staff had not previously imagined possible. I believe the matter is still talked about to this day: which is more than I can say about my attitude to Kreb's cycle.

So, after a short ride on the BART to Montgomery, Gabriella and I traipsed down to Mission, turned left, wandered for a couple of blocks and then entered one of those tall glass buildings that seem very popular in that neighbourhood. Not awfully keen on such things myself, but this one had a nice foyer with one of the largest indoor murals I had ever seen. There then followed a very fast ride to the eighteenth floor and, after a moment or two to bring my innards back up from my buttocks, we passed through a couple of doors that were opened by some sort of a security tag.

As we had arrived about fifteen minutes before kick-off, Gabriella suggested that I might like to have a seat and a cup of coffee. I agreed, and settled my hindquarters into a very comfortable armchair that afforded a splendid view out over the financial district of the City. I could see the Transamerica Pyramid – I didn't realise that the concrete columns on two of the sides (rather like handles) were housing structures for the lifts – and the Bank of America building, the Bay Bridge, and something that looked like a huge juke-box. All in all, not a skyline one could easily mistake for another one.

Gabriella soon returned with my beverage and asked if I would like to have a look through some of the legal magazines. Before I had time to elaborate upon my views of lawyers, she tossed a copy onto my lap and wandered off again. I flipped through only a few of the pages, and then my eyes alighted on a photograph of three – who I assumed to be top flight - corporate litigants.

"Nothing unusual about that," I hear you murmur. "It was a law magazine. What were you expecting? Photographs of farm machinery?"

There was nothing wrong with the subject matter in the photograph; but it was the legend that came with the photograph that caught my attention. Not merely because of what was written, but also because it looked patently untrue.

The three gentlemen concerned looked upright, both literally and metaphorically, and yet they were being described as the 'Mightily Pissed of Whatnot and partners'. I have left out the names in order to avoid encouraging their litigious pursuits in my direction.

I would have thought 'Slightly Inebriated' or, possibly, 'Marginally Squiffy'; but *Mightily Pissed?* Seemed a bit strong to me: a bit too much of an invite for a courtroom slugging match. But hey ho, as they say.

Further contemplation was avoided by a gentle tap on my right shoulder, and I duly followed Gabriella to our seats; from where we watched the edification unfold. Although, I suppose, that wasn't quite true, as I shall shortly enlighten you. But first things first.

Our compère for the evening was a rather short gentleman who was hailed by the name of Herman Windbigler, and that, quite obviously, was a less than propitious way to begin. Not that I have anything against a name like Herman Windbigler, and I am quite sure that there are places on this wonderful planet of ours where such an appellation would be deemed a distinct honour. I, however, have never had the pleasure of visiting any such places, and fair struggled to prevent myself from slapping my thigh and laughing out aloud.

I do, however – as I think I may have mentioned - possess certain views about short men. Nothing about their lack of inches per se, just the incredible amount of psychoses that so often seem to accompany such a dearth of inches in the personal elevation department.

True, to these unfortunates the world must seem full of people who look down upon them: true, their growing days (or shortage thereof) must have seemed full of children who had little else to do apart from give them less than flattering sobriquets: and true, I presume, it can't have been much fun getting continually clouted round the head by teachers for appearing not to stand up when they came into the room.

I was going to make some observation about drawbacks concerning the dating of members of the fairer sex, but I think that when dancing with a taller woman you usually have somewhere comfortable to rest your head should you ever feel bejaded. But all of that pales into insignificance when I mention that Herman had a third cross to bear. He was wearing, what in that part of the world is referred to as, a rug.

Now I have every sympathy with those among us who, for one ill-fated reason or another, have lost their scalp hair and, anxious to avoid ridicule or temperature loss, have had recourse to donning a wig. I always advise to look for any accompanying loss of eyebrow hair for this, if apparent, should act as a strong

261

indication that the depilation has occurred as a result of alopecia or the undergoing of anti-cancer treatment, rather being dealt a genetically poor hand. Consequently, such infelicitous individuals should be spared any and all ribaldry.

But those individuals, however, who choose to place a dead marsupial on their cranium in the hope that the rest of their fellow men are going to be fooled into thinking that they possess a full head of healthy tresses are fair game. I base my criticism on two fronts.

Firstly, that the wearer of the article of deception almost always looks ridiculous – especially when the hair is of an obviously different colour and bares more than a passing resemblance to a small woodland creature that chose the top of their head as a good place to draw its last breath. As for those ensembles that are similar to a cross between a bird's nest and candyfloss ... Well, I'm not sure if the world has enough space for all the opprobrium warranted.

Secondly, and possibly worse, is the affront intended by imagining that I, or anyone with even a modicum of intelligence for that matter, has been hoodwinked into thinking that all is well in the pelt department.

But, magnanimously, I managed to push all my preconceptions to one side, and let the class commence.

"Okay," Herman began, after having introduced himself and the purpose of the evening. "How many people here have ever had problems with a job interview?"

Everybody's hand, bar either of those belonging to yours truly, went up.

"And how many of you felt that was due to a defect in your technique?"

Same result.

"You sir, your name?"

"Joseph Klitgaard."

I beg your pardon, I thought. *Where do these names originate? And how? And how on earth do they ever manage to -*

"Okay. Right, let's begin with you. But I would like the rest of the group to look through the guide notes that you found on your seats at the same time. Have a look at the key interview questions, and you will see that they are designed to find your weaknesses and strengths. Okay, Joe ... May I call you Joe?"

"Yes sir."

"Great. Okay, let's begin with the first impressions, and all those non-verbal signals."

"Yes sir."

"So, what forms part of the first impression?"

"Appearance, sir."

"Right ... Go on."

"One should be dressed appropriately."

"That's good. Does anybody know what inappropriate dress for an interview might be?"

A forest of hands sprang up, and a flurry of answers followed as Herman's finger pointed at those attached to the arms raised. 'Casual slacks', 'Very short skirt', 'No tie', 'Tuxedo' (that

263

managed to raise a few laughs – can't think why; after all, the job may have been for a wine waiter), and several others that belonged in the 'logical but hardly amusing' category. Finally, and almost inevitably, the finger was aimed at my good self.

"You sir."

"Yes?"

"Do you have any inappropriate attire you'd like to mention?"

"I hardly think," I replied, "that details of my private life are matters for public consumption."

"Excuse me?"

"If my wardrobe contains garments that might, for whatever reason, be considered inappropriate, I should prefer, if you don't mind, to keep the matter as private as possible."

"I ... you ..."

"Quite."

"I mean do you have any inappropriate attire that I might wear for an interview?"

"Possibly, but I doubt very much if it would fit. Rather on the long side for you, I should imagine."

"What? No, I meant can you think of something *you* might wear for an interview that might be considered inappropriate?"

"Hmm. Such as scuba gear, perhaps?"

"And you might normally wear something like that?"

"Not normally, no. But, I suppose if the advertised position was for a North Sea oil rig repairman, then I should imagine the answer would be yes."

"If the – Okay ... let's think about the next aspect. Anybody?"

"Maintaining eye contact?" asked a stringy-looking fellow near the front.

"Good. And you are ...?"

"Robert Ingarbart."

"May I call you Bob?"

"Sure."

"Well, Bob, you have raised a good issue. Eye contact. Most important. Look straight at the questioner. Let him know you have strength. Commitment. But don't stare. Don't try and intimidate. Anything else?"

"Sit well?" came another voice.

"Good. And you are ...?"

"Richard Ringmold III."

"Explain."

"Well, my father is Richard Ringmold II, and his father was -"

"No, ha-ha, explain what you mean by 'sitting well'. And may I call you Dick?"

Dick Ringmold! I thought, as I hurriedly started packing the wide end of my tie into my mouth. *Oh dear, oh dear, oh dear!*

"Surely. I mean that one should sit in an upright position, avoid excessive hand movements, and try and keep any nervous tics down to a minimum."

"Good."

Good? I was so glad that I hadn't paid to come and sit through a series of what could accurately be described as the list of 'bleeding obvious' techniques for not making a complete arse of yourself. Apart from, of course, the Dick Ringmold coup de maître. I think that I would pay good money to be able to put that epithet on my job application form.

"Okay then," Herman continued. "Now I would like you to have a read through the examples of questions that you are likely to encounter at a job interview."

I would have thought, before even looking, that the list was going to be fairly predictable. After all, I couldn't imagine the interviewers being particularly concerned about what the interviewee did during his summer holiday. Unless, of course, it involved a series of unsavoury acts with such as farmyard animals.

265

I turned the pages of the notes, and found that Herman had divided them into two main categories ... To find major weakness and to find major strengths.

Key questions for finding weaknesses –

1) What do you feel are your major weaknesses?
2) What has been your single most significant work-related failure to date? Why?
3) From a work-related standpoint, what is your biggest shortcoming? And why?
4) If we asked 2 or 3 of your co-workers to identify areas in which you could most improve, what would they choose?
5) If you could, what 2 or 3 things would you most like to change about yourself to improve your work effectiveness? And why?

Apparently, so Herman then informed us, the bosses are looking for three main target areas regarding one's shortcomings - Technical, Interpersonal, and Personal. It seemed to me as though they were looking for a reason not to employ you in the first place.

Herman went on to say that one should choose shortcomings that are not too severe, pick weaknesses that are least related to key aspects of the job, and try to pick weaknesses that could be seen as strengths.

I would have thought that the first piece of advice was rather obvious. I mean, who is going to say that their major weaknesses include arson, larceny, and an insatiable desire to urinate into waste-paper baskets? Actually, a chap I once knew - his name escapes me at the moment, but I'm sure he'll recognise himself - might include those foibles amongst his many.

As for one's single most significant work-related failure to date ... *To date?* That, to me, implies there could be more to come.

"Hmm," one might say, "Let me think ... Oh yes, there was the time I e-mailed all that sensitive data to one of our main competitors by mistake. But hey, that's going to seem small beer compared to the clanger I have in mind for next year."

If we asked 2 or 3 of your work colleagues about you ... I would imagine that might rather depend on whom you asked. I could see that this was heading towards an evening centring on 'The joys of using a torch in daylight': and I was not mistaken.

Choose shortcomings that are not too severe. Like what? My aggressive tendencies are now controlled by medication?

Pick weaknesses that are least related to key aspects of the job. Such as? I tend to break a lot of wind?

And as for what one might change about oneself in order to improve one's work effectiveness! How about ... I am on the cusp of overcoming narcolepsy and alcoholism? Fairly essential factors I should have thought: especially if the position was that of a commercial pilot!

But Herman had answers arranged, and written down, for us to read.

1)   'My two greatest job-related weaknesses are that I tend to be highly focussed and results-oriented'.
     I beg your pardon? Weaknesses? I had supposed that those 'traits' would have been quite useful.
2)   'I can be a bit too brief in report writing, but this has not been an area of major concern as my boss has every confidence in my technical ability. What I am learning is that my boss needs better documentation. I can't blame him for that, so I am making a real effort to give him what he needs'.

What ever happened to the days of judging a fellow by the cut of his jib? I don't suppose I would have ever achieved gainful employment if I had to jump through hoops such as those. Never have been much of a groveller, I'm afraid. But there was more to come - in the shape of questions designed to help the interviewers identify key strengths, key strength utilisation, and comparison with peers. Oh, dear Lord, give me strength.

1) What do you consider your greatest strengths or assets?
2) What factors most account for your career success to date?
3) What do you consider your most outstanding quality?
4) In what areas are others complimentary of you?
5) What single skill or capability has most contributed to your career success?

I would like, at this point, to stick my thumbs behind my jacket lapels and twiddle my fingers. Unfortunately, I cannot be sure if -

1) I can hold my breath for ninety seconds.
2) I made a lot of influential friends whilst at school.
3) I have a rather charming boyish smile.
4) I always pay for my fair share of drinks.
5) I can recite Kipling's 'If' whilst balancing a pint of beer on my head.

- would really help in an American-style job interview. But there we are. Herman, once again, told us of an ideal response.

"My three major strengths are that I am creative, results-oriented (*I thought he had marked that down as a weakness*), and continuous-improvement driven (*and you do seem like a borderline emetic*). My whole approach to work is one where I purposely review how work is being done to look for those improvement opportunities that will have the greatest impact. Identifying the major barriers to improvement in those areas, I then look for creative ways to eliminate those barriers and move on to bring the improvement about."

268

Well, apart from wanting to point out his grammatical shortcomings, I also wanted to prevent myself from being sick. I think Gabriella must have noticed my rather bemused expression and, perhaps, sensed that I was about to make an enlightening comment, for she suddenly placed one of her hands upon one of my thighs.

It had hitherto escaped my notice, but do you know, I think I must have some kind of hidden circuit-breaker in that region. At the precise moment of contact, all my thought processes ceased forthwith, and whatever pearls of wisdom I had intended to impart to the assembled apprentices seemed to vanish into the ether. It was really most peculiar.

Then, while I was contemplating my new-found physiology, Herman decided to tell us all about the part of the interview strategy that concerned presentation, greeting and body language. He also decided that it might be nice to use a member of the group to help him demonstrate the points upon which he wished to elaborate. Unfortunately, he decided that member would be me; and before either Gabriella or I could explain to him why he had not chosen wisely, I was encouraged out of my chair and beckoned to the front of the assemblage. A small round of sympathetic applause accompanied me.

"Thank you, sir," Herman said, smiling obsequiously.

"You're welcome."

"And your name is ...?"

"William Phalarope."

"William ... Phalarope. May I call you Bill?"

"No."

"No?"

"No."

"Oh. Okay, er, William. Are you familiar with job interviews?"

"Not really."

"Oh. Right. Well, for the purpose of this exercise I am going to be your prospective employer, and you are going to be the candidate for the job I'm offering. Is that okay?"

"I would imagine so."

"Hey! Are you English?"

"Indeed I am."

"Great. That should make this a really good exercise." Herman turned to the others and gave one of those ingratiating - some might say 'irritating' - smiles. "Well, I'm going to take my seat, and you're going to come into the room, as if for the interview. Okay?"

"So far."

Herman then sat down on the other side of the desk and said, "Come in."

"Right-ho," I replied, closing an imaginary door behind me, which educed a small ripple of mirth from the onlookers.

"Have a seat."

"Thank you."

"Okay ... and you are ...?"

"William Phalarope."

Herman then sat quietly for a moment, looking at me.

"William Phalarope," I felt compelled to repeat; a bit louder.

"No, that's okay, William. I heard you. I was just waiting for your opening."

"My opening? What opening? The door? Do you want me to go back out again?"

"No, William. I want to hear what you have to say to me."

"What about?"

"Let's start off with who you are."

"I've already told you. I'm William Phalarope."

"Right ... Is there more?"

"No: just William Phalarope. My parents couldn't agree on another name."

"Excuse me?"

"My parents decided that William was sufficient."

"They - No, William, this is nothing to do with what you're called. I want you to begin with what you imagine is the best greeting opening. Sell yourself to me."

"Why?"

"You want the job, don't you?"

"I think that rather depends on what it is."

"Depends on what- It doesn't matter what the job is."

"It does to me."

"It doesn't matter for this exercise. It's just an exercise. To show you the techniques that you should use. That's all. Okay?"

"Oh. Right."

"Now where are you going?"

"I'm going to start again."

"No, don't worry about that. Just sit back down. Take it from where you were. Sell yourself."

"Got you. Okay. Yes. Er ... Hello."

"Hello."

"Jolly decent of you to dangle the old 'sit vac' in front of me. Very much appreciated, I don't mind admitting."

"The *sit vac*?"

"Yes."

"And that is ...?"

"The job. The situation vacant, and so forth."

"Oh ... Okay. You're welcome."

"Thank you. So when would you like me to start pressing my conk to the grindstone?"

"What?"

"When do you want me to start work?"

"To start work! I don't know anything about you."

"So why did you ask me here?"

"To have an interview. I want you to impress me."

"There's not really much need for that, is there?"

"Why not?"

"Because I'm the only person here for the interview."

"That's because you were the only person I called out."

"Well there you are then … Res iudicata."

"What?"

"Res iudicata. A decided case. Is this not a law firm?"

"What? Why should it be a law firm?"

"I thought that most firms in San Francisco were law firms. All that suing and what-not going on."

"Look, it really doesn't matter what this firm is."

"Of course it does."

"Why? No, don't answer that. Look, William, maybe you had better be the interviewer, and I'll show you the sort of thing I want to hear from the interviewee. Will that be okay?"

"As you wish," I replied, swapping seats with Herman.

"Okay then?" Herman asked, as he sat down."

"Okay what?"

"Are you ready to hear what I have to say?"

"In just a moment."

"In just a moment?"

"Yes. I haven't asked you to come in yet."

"Oh for Pete's sake! This is just an exercise."

"I know that. I just thought you -"

"Don't think: just listen."

"As you wish."

"Good. Now then … My name is Herman Windbigler. Thank you for the opportunity to visit with you today. I'm really looking forward to discussing the opportunity you have presented for me to work as a promotional executive in your sales department. From what I've been told by the search team it sounds like an interesting position. So, William, how am I doing so far?"

"You're coming across as a bit of a crawler, actually. Not at all the sort of person I'd want working for me."

"What!"

"I want upright people in my firm. People with a solid backbone. People who play with a straight bat."

"A straight bat? A *straight bat?* What the - William, I am trying to get across the concept that I would be a benefit to your firm."

"Well you won't do it like that."

"What! Why not?"

"Because I really don't care for sycophants."

"You don't ... But that's the way that we do it over here."

"I'm sure it is. But you said that *I* was in charge of the firm, and I can assure you that no firm of mine would ever employ someone who grovels."

"Someone who -"

It was about this time that Herman began displaying several of the physical characteristics against which he had so thoroughly warned us. He didn't sit well, his eye contact was constant - and hovering somewhere between glaring and manic - several nervous tics had suddenly appeared from nowhere, and he seemed to be indulging in an awful lot of hand movements. I felt that my decision not to offer him the position was fully vindicated.

Gabriella then got to her feet and pointed towards the door: quite sternly, as I recall. I raised my eyebrows in a questioning sort of way, as I wasn't clear what she meant.

"William." Gabriella used a tone of voice that matched the firmness of her index finger gesticulations.

"Hello there," I replied, quite keen to demonstrate a degree of cordiality.

"Here. Now."

"Quite," I said, taking the time to smile pleasantly at Herman as I stepped over him: he seemed to be taking a bit of a rest on the floor in front of the desk. An extraordinary way, I thought, for someone seeking gainful employment to conduct himself at an interview. San Francisco practices are a constant surprise to me.

Fleet Week and the Blue Angels.

Rumour had it that several ships belonging to the American navy were going to be making an appearance in the waters just off San Francisco – having sailed under the Golden Gate bridge – and that quite a good vantage was to be had by standing between Chrissy Field and Fisherman's Wharf.

So, on the appointed day, I took a cable-car to the bottom end of Hyde Street. There I found about half the inhabitants of the City, who had all, so it seemed, happened upon the same idea as myself. Undaunted, I strolled along the edge of Aquatic Park, marvelling at the ever-increasing throngs, and began heading towards Municipal Pier.

Bound to get a better view from there, I thought, neatly meandering between the others who were mainly concentrating on getting themselves outside their corndogs: and hotdogs, burgers, doughnuts, pretzels, and gallon upon gallon of fizzy drink.

Pausing at which point for a moment, I have to say that before leaving the UK I had been under the impression that three out of five citizens of the USA were on the lumpy side of proportionate. But I also have to say that I hadn't noticed anywhere near that ratio amongst the inhabitants of San Francisco. Perhaps it was because the City is a focus for 'beautiful people': perhaps it was because the aesthetic body shape is admired, or prized, more highly than in other areas. I do hope that attitude continues to prevail.

Eat less and do more exercise, is what I say. And to the majority of those corpulent individuals who plead that the fault lies with having big bones, hormone problems, glandular trouble, or being genetically disadvantaged, I say take a look at archive photographs of places like Dachau, Belsen and Auschwitz, where there were rows upon rows of emaciated human beings. You never saw half a dozen fat ones on the end saying "Oh, it's my glands." The vast (if you'll pardon the pun) majority of fat people are fat because they eat too much.

Now – before all those bleaters (or do I mean bloaters) come up with "But I don't eat a lot" - I have to emphasise the difference between 'too much' and 'a lot'. If you burn up 3000 calories a day and you consume 4000, you eat 'too much'. If you burn up 6000 calories a day and you consume 6000 calories, you eat 'a lot', but not 'too much'. As I said, simple: but nothing to do with Fleet Week.

One of the first things that struck me was what a lot of security types there were milling around. I certainly got the impression that many of our American friends enjoy swaggering about with their guns and holsters – Matt Dillons every one: but no room here to debate the joys of gun culture.

I realise that since the events of September the 11th 2001 the attitudes of most people have irrevocably changed – I can hear several conspiracy advocates mentioning that the whole episode was 'arranged' by the American government in order to frighten Americans into accepting a 'benign' form of Martial Law - but it did seem a shame to see so many 'official' personnel strutting their stuff, armed to the teeth with an extraordinary array of weaponry. I wasn't entirely sure what good automatic weapons were going to be against an aircraft crashing into the side of a building; but there we are.

Speaking of aircraft and buildings, it has been, for many years, an annual event where the Blue Angels (America's version of the Red Arrows) strafe San Francisco as part of the rehearsals for their display. Apparently the pilots have had a tendency to whiz between the buildings, showing off their skills, whilst scaring the proverbial out of the office workers.

I have sometimes wished that I had been able, either by virtue of sufficient dexterity or eyesight, to have pursued a career in flying. The glamour, the camaraderie, the flocks of admiring women: all matters to which I am sure I would have taken like a duck to water. But even if I had the eyes and the degree of co-ordination required, I fear that my organs of equilibrium would have let me down at every turn, quite literally, and the inside of my cockpit would have been rendered in a manner that would not have found universal approval.

However, to return to the planes and buildings, the previous year the rehearsal was cancelled. It seems that, since the events of September the 11th, people have been rather alarmed to see jet planes buzzing around tall buildings: especially if those same people happened to be inside the buildings. This year, a limited amount of strafing had been permitted and the aircraft duly arrived to do their practicing: and what a sight they were.

If one sees military-type jet aircraft in an environment that suits them, by that I mean some sort of combat situation, they appear normal. But see them weaving in and out of buildings and they take on another dimension. Not exactly scary – actually, scary might be the right word – but awesome. Yes, scary and awesome: and very loud.

I was sitting in the apartment when the planes first arrived. I was having a cup of tea (I took the precaution of taking tea-bags with me), minding my own business, and doing one of the broadsheet crosswords, when 'VOOOOM' ... all the windows shook. I nearly dropped my tea - I definitely spilled the plate of biscuits - as one of the planes shot past the window. Well, to be truthful, the plane didn't actually shoot 'past' the window - it flew overhead - but the effect was pretty much the same. So I grabbed my camera, and dashed up to the roof, hoping to get a photograph or two.

You would think that it would be jolly difficult for a jet aircraft to creep up on you – bearing in mind that they weren't flying anywhere near the speed of sound – but creep up was what they did. I think the reason was the enormously high buildings all around that not only hid the planes from view until they were practically on top of you, but also, because of the redirection of sound, they made it nigh on impossible to judge the location of the sound source.

What it must be like to have one of those blighters homing in at you – which is unnerving enough by itself – and knowing that it was about to drop something unpleasant in your vicinity, I do not care to imagine: but watching them rehearse their manoeuvres was very impressive. However, strangely enough, the manoeuvre that impressed me most of all was probably the most unhurried thing they did. I have no idea what it was called, but it involved flying the aircraft about one hundred feet above the water, tilting it so that its nose was up in the air – making the aircraft about forty-five degrees to the horizontal – and going incredibly slowly. The word 'stall' kept popping into my head.

Not what one would describe as spectacular – certainly not when compared with high-speed crossovers and what have you – but I have a feeling that a great deal of airmanship was involved all the same.

Anyway, to return to the fleet occasion, I made my way down to Municipal Pier; where I encountered a barrier of some description, manned by some rather stern-looking military types: and 'womanned' by some even sterner-looking individuals. It seemed that their collective presence was to check people who wanted to gain access to the pier, and then fix some kind of tag around their wrists. I approached with caution.

"Are you going on the pier?" asked a lady who looked as if she had learned how to bench-press under the tutelage of a certain Paul Anderson.

"Please."

"How long ya gonna be there?"

"Not very long."

"We only got seven tickets left."

"Oh. That's fine, there's only one of me."

"I can see that, but we're only lettin' people on who's gonna stay awhile."

"Awhile being …?"

"'Bout two or three hours."

"Well, what a coincidence."

"Huh?"

"My 'not very long', is about two or three hours."

"Say what?"

Seemed an odd request, but I complied. "What."

"What?"

"Quite."

"I said … Never mind, here."

With that, I duly had a small plastic bracelet clipped around my wrist and, with six other people, I was allowed to pass through.

Fleet Week involved several vessels of the United States navy coming into the Bay and, as well as a type of 'sail past', they moor up and allow citizens of San Francisco to go aboard to have a look round. A few years ago, so Gabriella informed me, people were allowed to go on as many vessels as they could manage: these days it seemed that it was all to be done by prior appointment with a maximum of one vessel per person. A bit of a shame, but there it is.

Anyway, I made my way along the pier until I reached another manned barrier; past which they were charging people to proceed: and not just a couple of dollars either. My fiscally-sensible blood then made a sudden surge through my cerebral arteries, and I declined the opportunity to go any further.

A quick reconnoitre of the area showed that the best viewing point was going to be had by standing on a raised concrete rim that ran the length of the area, and taking advantage of the shade offered by the portable chemical toilets.

A few minutes later I was aware of something large and grey emerging from the mist that hung like a stage curtain from the Golden Gate Bridge - it was the bow of the Aircraft Carrier USS Boxer. I don't suppose that the effect had been arranged, but it was very impressive all the same: and it also gave a very good indication of just how big the bridge is. The Golden Gate, that is, rather than the one on the Boxer.

It was then that all the 'whoopin' and 'a-hollerin' began. I am fairly sure that a British crowd would have waved a flag or two, raised a polite round of applause, maybe even given out 'three cheers': and that would have been fine. There may also have been a spontaneous chorus of 'Rule Britannia': although, thinking about the progressive (and deliberate) diminution of our Royal Navy (and all our Armed Forces for that matter) by that duplicitous bunch residing in halls of Westminster, perhaps not. Have I mentioned my antipathy towards our spineless Members of Parliament? They make my blood boil, they really do.

I, like many other truly British people, feel a certain warmth, and pride, in the history surrounding the British armed forces; and an unshakeable confidence in their ability to surpass any requirements asked of them. Unless, as I may have implied, some of our recent asinine politicians have been doing the asking.

Whilst I'm on the subject of British achievements, I can vividly remember, several years back, driving Eastwards along the M4 – about three miles on the English side of the new Severn Bridge – and seeing Concorde flying overhead. It was an absolutely magnificent sight and my chest fair swelled with pride. I will not go into the political shenanigans that went on to allow the French to become involved, but let's just say that – in my not inconsiderable opinion – some of our aforementioned dim-witted politicians had their fingerprints all over the affair.

Yes, give a good British mind a pencil and a blank sheet of paper and who knows what may result. I could go on about the likes of Faraday, Newton, Babbage, Whittle, Fleming, Baird, Watt, Stephenson, Wallis and so many more that I would probably run out of ink; but I will merely say that such as they always make my chest inflate. I just wish that some of the lefty-liberal-wishywashy-trendies would let our schoolchildren take a similar pride as well. Maybe I'll deal with that state of affairs another day.

Anyway ... whoopin' etc. Bad enough on its own, but when emanating from overweight men sporting baseball caps, knee-length (invariably checked – or should that be plaid?) shorts, ghastly-coloured socks and open sandals (might have been related to the fellow who enquired about food on Fisherman's Wharf) it is positively unbearable. More than ever when said perpetrators are trying to juggle with hamburgers the size of dinner plates, cola cups the size of buckets, and using accents and a command of the English language that would make George Bush Junior sound as if he had spent several years at RADA and Oxford.

Another one of those times when one can quite understand the antipathy shown towards the United States by many parts of the world. Yes, yes, I can hear all of you bleating about how the USA came to our aid during the last World War. But I can't hear too many of you explaining how the British got cheated out of ownership of most of the Trinidad and Tobago tarmac company and South American railways as a result of some shady 'lease-lend' deal involving three or four rust-buckets. Yet another discussion for another day, I imagine.

Mind you, perhaps I should also mention the work around 1944 by a fellow called Dennis Bancroft, the Miles M52 aircraft, a moving tailplane and the way that the Americans reneged on their promise - having looked at the British research data regarding breaking the sound barrier - to let us see what they had. Did Chuck Yeager say thank you? I'm not sure.

Anyway, I stood and enjoyed the sight of several vessels as they sailed past; their crew on deck, resplendent in their white uniforms, as helicopters flew over, and water cannon sprays formed rainbows. But only for about forty-five minutes: the smell of onions and beer, and gratingly annoying jingoism finally got to me.

I get to sing with my supper.

Eventually, as with most things, my trip soon reached its conclusion. One more night, and then I was due at the airport for a 4.30 pm flight back to the UK. Gabriella thought that it might be rather a nice idea for us to have my final evening in a place she sometimes visited.

"Sounds good to me," I said, always one to fit in with my host, as we walked towards Union Square.

"Are you okay with things that have an Irish connection?" Gabriella asked, hesitantly, as we paused outside a particular eatery.

I have to admit to having one or two reservations about going to any place that had some kind of an Irish connection. Not on any plausible grounds I hurriedly add; just based on years of prejudice against Irish accents and the number of unpleasant Irish people who have dropped into my life from time to time.

281

Yes, I know that there are thousands of incredibly nice Irish people - just as there are thousands of incredibly unpleasant English people - it's just that not many of them have ever made their presence known to me.

Speaking of accents; have you noticed how many television adverts use a Scottish accent? I understand that it is due to some research – done a few years ago I should imagine - which showed that most people find a Scottish accent to be trustworthy. I don't know about you, but ever since we have had so many MPs with Scottish accents in charge, I have associated a Scottish accent with someone who is being - how shall I put it - economical with the truth. Absolutely guaranteed to put me off buying the product. But there we are. Would this be a good place to mention the Barnett Formula or the West Lothian Question? Probably not. Anyway, where was I? Oh yes.

"I can be … I expect," I replied.

"Good. Let's go then," she said and went in.

Pushing preconceptions to one side, I followed, and – although not exactly expecting Leprechauns and people bashing each other over the heads with shillelaghs – I was a bit surprised to see that the only subject matter inside was posters of baseball players. Perhaps the only Irish connection was the name of the place; and I felt I could live with that.

Gabriella and I collected a couple of large beef sandwiches (although 'rolls' would have been a more accurate description) – with one side of the roll dipped in gravy – and sat at a vacant table. A pleasant young girl came and took our drinks order, and we tucked in.

And very nice it was too; although I wasn't too thrilled with the choice of mustards that they had on offer. Why can't Americans understand that the mustard served with beef should be English mustard? Yes, whole grain is very nice; yes, Dijon has a place as well - the American stuff is a bit too much like custard for my liking – but good old Colman's English is the one that hits the spot.

Anyway, along with the enormous beef roll, I managed to imbibe a couple of pints of beer, and all felt well with the World. Gabriella suggested that we might move a bit closer to the source of the live music - a piano - and so we did.

Now, for some reason best known to certain covalently bonded hydroxyl groups, when I have had a glass or two I not only think that I have rather a good baritone singing voice but I feel that I ought to allow people loitering within earshot to enjoy my dulcet tones.

The piano was stationed between the two entrances, and most evenings they supply someone prepared to thump the ivories whilst another inflicts their singing upon the unsuspecting patrons. This particular evening I decided, with a little encouragement from Gabriella, that I should vibrate my chordae vocalis and bring a little more pleasure into the lives of the gathered customers.

Have you noticed how, even with the best will in the world, a singer cannot help but appear egotistical: particularly when going through the normal warm-up procedure. There is something about hearing a person chanting "Me-me-me-me-me," that inclines one to imagine that a certain degree of self-admiration is involved: and, I have to say, there usually is.

I suppose, grammatically, it really ought to be "I-I-I-I-I.", but that, I have found, often leads others to believe that certain parts of Carmen Miranda's repertoire are to be included. It is always a tad embarrassing when the assembled audience spend a moment or two balancing bowls of fruit on their heads in anticipation, and you then give them a sterling rendition of 'I've got me ten fine toes to wriggle in the sand'.

Another very strange thing about the effect that alcohol has upon me – apart from the already mentioned urge to warble – is that not only do my jokes become funnier, but the women present seem to get prettier. Maybe it's the way that their faces soften with all the laughter.

Anyway, back to the piano. The instrumentalist wanted to know in which key I preferred to sing. At this point I ought to mention that I have never felt compelled to stick to any one key when intoning, as that has always seemed such a waste when there are so many that you can use. I might start off in 'G', then flirt for a moment in 'F' and 'C', before finishing my performance with 'E'.

"And so what?" I ask. The keys are there to be enjoyed, and I think that as long as one can hang on to the original melody, most people are more than happy to sit back and let the notes arrive: certainly if they, too, have had a few drinks.

In places like La Scala, obviously, it is usually considered fitting that the correct notes, in the correct order, are produced; and at such a volume as to allow auditory access to those patrons whose finances only allow them to occupy seats requiring the use of lorgnettes. But, I felt, in my present whereabouts I could surely avail myself of whichever key was nearest to hand.

I think I got off to a fairly good start. Well, in so much as nothing other than a paper airplane got thrown in my direction: and that came from a fellow who was drinking from a glass with a small umbrella in it, so I didn't have any reason to think that I had been singled out for the mistreatment of notes.

But then matters began to take a turn for the worse. Maybe I was off key slightly too much for people's liking, maybe the audience had grown weary of the timbre of my voice, maybe it was my choice of song – I thought that a rousing rendition of 'Land of Hope and Glory' would go down a treat.

I cannot be entirely sure, but I have thought about the incident on several occasions since, and I can find no fault with either Elgar's music or Arthur C. Benson's words. After all, many a time I have been to watch an international match at Twickenham and have, along with tens of thousands of like-minded individuals, taken a certain pride in belting out about how beneficial it would be for everybody if our bounds were to be set wider still and wider.

Perhaps, as a further thought has just entered my centres of reasoning, it could have been the fact that our American friends – at least those who were present at the time – felt slightly resentful of the British heritage and wished to express their vexation in a manner that best exemplified their character. Or maybe I had underestimated the strength of feelings of the Irish contingent present. Who knows?

A fellow can dodge bread rolls with alacrity, and napkins soaked in beer with consummate ease; he can even find witty retorts to signed petitions for him to seek gainful employment in another part of the country. However, I felt justified in calling it a day when items of cutlery started arriving.

You see, I am one of those troubadours who, for whatever reason, finds it rather hard to concentrate on the words whilst being assailed by a selection of knives, forks, and some rather ornate mustard spoons; and I decided that a strategic cessation to my vocal offering might be prudent.  Especially as the pianist was now bleeding from a small wound to his forehead caused by a misdirected cruet set.

It was also about this time that I felt a tugging sensation on my right trouser leg; and a glance in that direction showed me that Gabriella was the cause.

"Get down," she hissed, pulling with a strength that belied her slender frame.

"Goodness," I replied, crouching under the piano beside her. "Does it often get this rowdy?"

"I've never seen it get -"

The rest of her answer was interrupted by the sound of what felt like somebody being thrown onto the piano, and several beer glasses following suite. It seemed that a free-for-all on a fairly large scale had now developed due, I was to discover when reading the papers at the airport, to the fact that several members of a rugby club from Cornwall had been enjoying my rendition and took exception to the general reaction to my performance shown by others in the establishment.

Had I known that I was not alone, I might well have stayed to exchange pugilistic skills with several of those involved in the fracas. But before I had time to assess the situation, Gabriella convinced me that discretion would be the better part of valour, and a diplomatic exit – by means of a crawling motion – was a pretty good way of ensuring that I caught my plane the next day.

"Ah," I hear you ask, "What about the fate of those intrepid Cornishmen?"

"No cause for distress there," I reply; for during some of the verbal interludes, the protagonists decided that the Irish and the Cornish had a mutual loathing of people with educated accents; so they shook hands and settled down to enthusiastic reciprocal back-slapping, multiple toasting, and were singing all manner of Celtic shanties by the time the police arrived.

As most of the officers summoned were of one sort of Gaelic descent or another, no charges were brought (apart from those to pay for repairs) and a pleasant evening of drink and 'English-bashing' was thus enjoyed.

<u>The flight Home.</u>

The following morning I decided – in order, once again, to try and get a seat with sufficient room for my legs – that it would be a good idea for me to arrive at the airport about an hour or so before the check-in desk opened for business. However, as with quite a lot of my good intentions, things did not go according to plan.

When I made arrangements to catch a minibus to go from the apartment to the airport, I did not realise that the apartment was the first pickup point on the list. This on its own was bad enough, as it meant that I would spend a good deal longer in the vehicle than I had anticipated; but I was, however, further inconvenienced by the fact that the driver, for some unfathomable reason, thought I was an entertainment impresario who had chosen a courier bus as a likely place to discover new talent.

It has long been my impression that amateur voices tend to fall into one of four main categories. Firstly, there is the out-and-out, venue-filling boomer who can hit notes - not always the right ones, mind you - from any distance. Secondly, there is the fellow who thinks he sounds like a cross between Bing Crosby and Dean Martin, finds every opportunity to warble – rather like those blighters who think the whole world wants to hear them whistle – and is under the impression that every line of the song needs to end with 'hub-bub-ba-ba'. Thirdly, is what I describe as the 'pub singer' – the chap who likes to sing such enchanting refrains as 'My Way' - in fact it nearly always is My Way - and believes that the number is somehow enhanced by adding the sound 'ah' at the end of every line. By that I mean ...

"And now-ah,
    The end is near-ah,
        And so I face-ah,
            The final curtain-ah ..."

The driver of the courier bus, however, was one of those whose voice landed squarely in the fourth - the 'stage musical' category. A voice - and I have to point out to all libel case practitioners that it is merely my personal opinion - that can reach three notes very loudly and, somehow, attempts to negotiate songs using just those same three notes.

Why, I often ask myself, do the owners of such voices also seem to be under the impression that introducing a little vibrato and adjusting their facial expression alters the note in some way. Perhaps make it sound a little higher, they imagine: perhaps a little lower? But I can assure them that it does not. The usual result is that people like me start wondering if the singer is having some variety of stomach cramps, before we then rush off to extinguish any nearby naked flames.

Quite why the driver decided that I might be on the lookout for fresh talent I have no idea. Perhaps it was simply that he thought that I looked too cheerful to be leaving the City and my alacrity needing toning down a touch. Regardless, I studiously avoided comment: even when he turned his torso through more than ninety degrees to give me maximum decibels for his rendition of 'Oklahoma'. Although I avoided commenting on the noise he was making, I did draw his attention to one of several cars towards which we were travelling in a head-on fashion.

You will notice that I have left out all varieties of the infection known as 'pop singing', as I do not believe that 'voice' comes even close to describe the cacophony of auricular irritants that emanate from the faces of most people who perpetrate such a vile crime. Ghastly to a degree, they are.

Anyway, the net result of the final tour of San Francisco hotels and the extemporised auditions was that, instead of arriving before the check-in opened, I arrived about twenty minutes after and, as a consequence, I missed the opportunity to bag one of the doorway seats. Well, that and the rather over-officious young man who demanded, in a most impolite fashion, if he could see my passport.

288

"You were born in Ceylon?" he asked, a little too incredulously for my liking.

"Yes."

"Where's that?"

Oh dear. "It's an island off the southern tip of India."

"Isn't that Shree Lie-unka?"

Why do people insist on pronouncing Sri as 'Shree'? Or even Sur-ee?

"It is now known as Sri Lanka, but it was called Ceylon when I was born there."

"Is it British?"

"It was."

"Are you travelling alone?"

"I imagine that there will be others on the aircraft," I replied, thinking a little bit of levity might 'jolly up' the young man. I was wrong.

"Huh?" he said, his eyebrows coming together with such force that I'm sure they made a noise. "Are you try-yun to be fun-nah?"

"Me? Good Lord no," I hastily - and seriously - replied, as visions of an impromptu body search swam before my eyes. "Perish the thought."

"Yeah. Well, you have a good flight."

"Yes, I do hope so. Thank you."

I duly checked in, expressed as much pathos as I felt appropriate upon hearing the news that all the door seats had gone, and, with shoulders slightly hunched, began to move away from the counter. The young lady must have thought I looked quite distraught as, within a few seconds, she called me back.

Aha, I thought, eat your heart out, Sir Larry.

"We can arrange an up-grade for you, if you like, sir."

"A what?"

"An up-grade."

"And that is ...?"

"Where we move you up from Economy to Business class."

"The advantage being …?"

"A lot more leg room."

"Ah. And the catch being …?"

"A small charge."

"Which is …?"

The young lady quoted a sum that seemed just about acceptable and, after completing the financial arrangements, I was allocated a seat with more leg room. But I still had over two hours before take-off.

As I wrote earlier, I am not the world's greatest traveller: I have a tendency to if not *actually* part company with my last meal, then at least spend a large part of the trip wondering if I am about to do so. A none-too-pleasant state of affairs; either for myself, or those in the immediate vicinity.

However, I knew that liquids tend to stay in the stomach for a lot less time than solids - perhaps several minutes as against several hours - so it seemed quite a wise move not to have any solids in the time left before take-off.

But that, of course, might mean twelve or more hours without nourishment. I realise that twelve or more minutes without nourishment would be purgatory for some, whilst others could cheerfully go twelve or more days: but I am one of that happy band who like to stretch the gastric membranes about three times a day.

Bit of a quandary. But I needn't have worried as, soon after realising the problem, my centres of higher thinking came up with rather a good solution. Instead of putting solids inside my stomach, why not put a highly nutritional liquid there instead? Clever, eh? Well, I thought so.

"What on earth are you talking about?" I hear.

I'm talking about evaporated milk. An average can of the stuff contains a good helping of carbohydrates, protein, and around 650 calories; and that certainly seemed like the sort of boost that the owner of a potentially unstable digestive tract would appreciate. So there we are; a great idea: and I put this into practice whilst waiting in the departure area of SFO airport. I shall further add that I then felt a good deal more confident about completing the trip without examining the inside of a brown paper bag.

It was therefore with a nonchalant swagger that I boarded the aircraft, further boosted by being shown to the stairs that led to the upper deck. I have to admit, with much possibility of wrath-incurring from the socialist end of the readers' spectrum (but I don't care), that there is a certain cachet to be gained, and enjoyed, from a specified degree of segregation from the hoi polloi. As well as all the benefits of having more space, more comfort, and smaller queues for the toilet facilities.

But one is still going to be subject to the vagaries of fortune when it comes to the identity of the person who occupies the seat next to yours: and on this particular occasion Lady Luck decided to play a little game with William Phalarope.

No sooner had I sat down — my seat was next to the window — than a very attractive woman came and occupied the one alongside me. *Jolly good*, I thought. At least if I am unable to indulge in meaningful conversation, I can always enjoy the view.

And, no I am not going to elucidate on whether I meant the view to my left (woman) or my right (window), as I wish to keep any rampant feminists guessing and unable to vent any more of their pent-up spleen in my direction.

However, as I alluded to earlier, fortuity was merely being waggled in front of me on a temporary basis. A moment later a well-meaning stewardess came and told the attractive woman that, as the result of a little bit of seat-juggling, she was now able to sit next to her boyfriend. My spirits dropped slightly as the lady sashayed off to park her posterior next to the aforementioned companion; and then positively plummeted when her replacement arrived.

As I may have intimated on a previous occasion, I am not often one to speak ill of others, but when the seat next to me became occupied I felt inclined to ask for a full refund. I am all for giving a stranger the benefit of the doubt – as far as any latent nefarious qualities might be concerned – until I have cause to believe otherwise: but dash it all, there are times when one's bonhomie doesn't even reach the starting line-up.

And this was one such time.

I think I ought to point out that I have no formal training in the study of genetics, and wouldn't recognise an autosome if it came along and bit me on the ankle; but I would venture to say that the gentleman who came and sat next to me was definitely on the short side of his expected allotment of forty-six chromosomes.

As to which ones he might have misplaced I have no idea, but misplace them he most definitely had. Not that there was any glaringly obvious indication that Mother Nature had not been dealing with a full deck, but my years at a Public School had not been a complete waste: I have usually been able to spot a quiproquo when one comes along. But not, unfortunately, until the mistake has actually sat down beside me.

Yes, I am almost certainly being very whatever the appropriate word that ends in 'ist' is; yes, I most likely should thank my lucky stars, and say things such as "There but for gratia Dei go I"; and no, I probably should not have looked as if someone had just shoved a broom-handle up my fundament. But I did, so there we are.

Now, what can I tell you about flight back? Apart from, that is, keeping one eye on my neighbour.

Well, as the plane took off I have to admit that I found a certain ditty by Messrs Cross and Cory meandering its way through my grey matter, and a twinge of regret was knocking on the door of my consciousness. And that is not, I have to say, a brace of phenomena that normally arises with me. I was, however, unable to dwell on them for too long as matters concerning my neighbour began to take shape.

As I have mentioned, I prefer not to eat on the flight. I would *like* to eat; but, as I have also mentioned, I don't have complete confidence in the retentive abilities of my cardiac sphincter. My companion, on the other hand, was quite obviously not hampered by any such caveats, and never stopped consuming. Every time I checked to see what he was up to, it seemed he was in the process of moving comestibles from his plate with the aid of a plastic fork, or spoon, or knife, to the chasm that was loitering below his nose.

I would normally have just said 'eating', but the fellow seemed to be having a bit of trouble in finding his mouth: which was hard to understand, as you could have fitted a decent-sized dictionary into the space that was available. For some reason best known to his centres of co-ordination, there appeared to be a bit of a problem between the food leaving the plate and arriving at his oral cavity: and I don't think the pilot of our aircraft could be blamed.

I would, at a conservative estimate, have guessed that about a third of the material designated for arrival at the molar region missed the target altogether, and ended up either on the floor or all over the fellow's lap: and he seemed totally oblivious to it all. Then, as if such actions weren't enough to cause concern, he thought it would be a jolly good idea to precariously balance a full glass of water (he'd already polished off about four glasses of wine) on the arm of his chair: the arm that was closest to me.

Something inside me said – very loudly as it happens – that the glass was not going to remain there until the fellow wanted to drink the water. That same something also told me that a lot of the H_2O was going to be heading in my direction; and that was something I could well do without.

Now, how – without appearing a tad rude - does one tell another one that the first one (me) has absolutely no confidence in the second one's (his) ability to pass another five minutes (never mind five hours) without safely finding the water a second home? Or that the alternative accommodation was highly likely to be the front of my trousers? And, just to add a certain piquancy, to do so in the knowledge that the second one (him) has absolutely no idea about the problem he is demonstrating with his co-ordination, and that he (him) is roughly twice the size of the first one (me).

I decided to combine tact with a desire to avoid a clot in one of my deep veins – names like popliteal and tibial kept making guest appearances in my head – and conveyed a desire to leave my seat for a short stroll around the deck. The chap with the unfortunate synchronization problem seemed gracious enough about my request, and allowed me to pass by; and that manoeuvre, I might add, was completed without touching his glass.

I then spent several minutes (about fifteen actually) casually meandering about, smiling as I wandered hither and thither, happy in the knowledge that doing so made me less likely to get a glass of water over my trousers; and that my 'Christmas' and 'Stuart' factors were more likely to keep their heads down and not cause any discomfort within my circulatory system.

It's a very rum state of affairs - this thing they call 'Economy Class Syndrome'. Now I think of it, I shouldn't really have worried – being, as I was, in Business Class: but, I would like to know, why do we (well, I) never seem to hear of it happening to people who spend many hours driving? Or fishing? Or whole evenings spent sitting in front of the television? Is it, perhaps, because there is little chance of suing anybody for compensation under those circumstances?

I am quite sure that I once read, somewhere, about lots of people in London suffering DVTs during the Second World War – from long nights spent sitting on deck-chairs in underground stations whilst the Germans dropped bombs from above. I assume that I'm right in thinking that the phenomenon is not exactly a new one.

Speaking of new phenomena – what about people wishing to sue the manufacturers of cigarettes regarding the effects of smoking? Did they not know about the less than wholesome consequences of drawing smoke into their lungs? I just cannot imagine how information like that passed them by unnoticed. I know that Prime Minister Harold Macmillan (back in 1956) covered up a report about the harmful effects of smoking – something to do with the potential loss of tax revenue to the Treasury – but even so.

My maternal grandfather used to describe cigarettes as 'coffin nails': and that was as far back as 1935. PG Wodehouse wrote a story concerning a character by the name of 'Rollo', and mentioned many effects as being the 'vices of smoking': and that book was published back in 1926. Yet here we are, eighty odd years later, and people are still claiming it has all come as a complete surprise.

Anyway, there I was, doing the occasional knee-bend, trying not to seem concerned about hanging around outside the toilets, and having a quick glance at the gentleman in the seat next to mine to see how he was coping with the glass of water. I'm not sure what sort of odds I might have got – regarding how soon the glass would get spilled – probably 7-3 on, and I think I might well have had a flutter.

I would have been quids in for, between my fourth and fifth glance, the glass had disappeared from view, and the gentleman had stood up and was in the process of wiping himself – and his seat – with several handfuls of paper tissues. Unfortunately for him, he seemed to be doing little else but spreading the bits of food matter that had lodged about various parts of his person all over various other parts as well.

I gave the situation another five minutes before venturing back: and that was when I encountered another dilemma. Have I mentioned that the gentleman was the possessor of a quite unusual strand of nasal hair? Possibly not; well he was. The strand in question was sticking out, in the region of three-quarters of an inch, was as straight as a die, and a silver colour. Rather as though he had a pin stuck up his nose, in fact. Very peculiar, and very hard from which to remove one's gaze.

I have a feeling that had I been in possession of a pair of pliers, I might well have removed said hair from said nostril. Might have been a bit risky, though, if the contents of his skull were as loosely held in place as they seemed to be. Not too sure how well that would have been received.

Anyway, I then had to spend the rest of the flight studiously ignoring my companion who was, by now, covered in damp clothes and food crumbs: and still had that pin sticking out of his nose. Very hard to concentrate on the film, I can tell you.

Was that to be the end of my inquietude? No it wasn't; for it seemed that there was a sprite loose about the aircraft which had decided that I needed something else to occupy my mind on the flight. Was it a crossword puzzle perhaps? No. How about an offer to join the 'Mile High' club? Not that either, I'm afraid.

It seemed that the fickle finger of fate had pointed at the nether regions of my companion and settled for an impromptu display of the art of flatulence that was to be as strident as it was malodorous. I can only imagine that I must have done something particularly heinous in a previous life: or perhaps one of my forebears, within the earlier three or four generations, had strayed from the straight and narrow.

Whatever the cause, I spent the rest of the flight employing two sets of earplugs: one set in the intended orifices, and the other in my nostrils. Worked a treat, and would have been the sort of advice that you could pass on to other people who find themselves in a similar situation: had it not been for the effect that it had on the stewardess the next time she stopped to ask if I wanted a drink.

The sudden start with which she jerked away when she saw what I had lodged in my nostrils would have been acceptable, and the stifled blurt of laughter may also have passed without comment. Unfortunately, the stewardess happened to be carrying a pitcher of water at the time, and managed to empty that and - as a result of being unable to control the snort that then emanated from within her nasopharynx - the contents of both her nostrils over the lady in front of me.

The resultant melee of activity - involving seat changes and a broadening of my expletive vocabulary - although somewhat alarming for those who had missed the opening scene, did seem to make the rest of the flight pass more quickly than it might otherwise have done.

Back home to reflect.

It has now been two weeks since I returned from the United States, and Jocelyn is due to call round this afternoon to conduct an interview with me about my experiences. I have a feeling that I may have to bowdlerise my answers to her questions as I fear that the unexpurgated version may attract unwanted legal repercussions.

I have had a go at guessing what her questions might be, and I doubt if I'll really be able to add anything more constructive than I had mentioned to her on the telephone. Well, certainly nothing that would be comprehended by the readers of her magazine. Or is that being a bit unkind? I suppose it might be, and I also suppose that my experiences in 'The City' have allowed me to recognise that.

Anyway, did I have fun? Yes.

Would I go again? Absolutely. Although I had better leave it long enough for people to have forgotten about me.

What memories stand out? Rather a lot actually. Big aspects like the grandeur and opulence seen in many parts of the City, and the abject poverty seen in so many others. The bizarreness of the Folsom Street Fair and the Defenestration on 6th and Howard. The joy at finding the jukebox in Café Trieste that only played opera, the uniqueness of Vivian and Marian Brown, the fun of Critical Mass, the history of Bummer and Lazarus, the enthusiasm of Hallowe'en, and the splendour of the Golden Gate Bridge.

As a by-product, I think I have taken on board the seemingly inexhaustible variety of human beings that there is to be found. Just when you think that you have seen them all, up pops another one. Fascinating, and no mistake: but I do find it hard to believe that God created all of them in His image!

I also want to mention the delightful Gabriela and the wonderful contribution that she made to the whole experience; I wish her well in all her future endeavours. I expect the fact that I am no longer within the City limits will help enormously.

But, maybe, most of all, was finding that San Francisco is a city that is not afraid to be what it wants to be. Long may it, and its inhabitants, survive and continue to help make this planet of ours a jolly sight more interesting than it might otherwise be. Yes, I think I can truthfully say that I was very lucky to have enjoyed the events that befell me during my stay. Gave the old ennui shelves a bit of a dusting, and that can never be a bad thing.

In fact, I rather think the Phalarope desire to sample new climes has had its cage rattled. Whatever next, I wonder?